AIR PILOT'S PRACTICAL & THEORETICAL WEATHER MANUAL

DAVID BRUFORD

Airlife
England

Meteorological charts are Crown copyright and reproduced with the kind permission of the Controller of Her Majesty's Stationery Office.

Icing chart, icing, thunderstorm, mountain wave and shear line diagrams reproduced with the assistance of the CAA Aeronautical Information Services, Heathrow.

Extract from *Heaven's Breath* by Lyall Watson reproduced by permission of Hodder & Stoughton Ltd/New English Library Ltd.

All references to Aeronautical Information Circulars quote the relevant issue at the time of publication, readers should note that these are subject to amendment.

First published in the UK in 1997 by Airlife Publishing Ltd.

British Catalogue-in Publication Data
A catalogue record for this book
is available from the British Library.

IBSN 1 85310 853 7

Typeset by Phoenix Typesetting, Ilkley, West Yorkshire.
Printed in England by Livesey Ltd, Shrewsbury.

Airlife Publishing Ltd
101 Longden Road, Shrewsbury SY3 9EB, England.

CONTENTS

Introduction

The Practical and Theoretical Weather Manual

Meteorology is the study of meteors which according to the Greek philosopher Aristotle were moist or dry vapours. He considered dry vapours to be thunder, lightning and the winds and moist vapours to be cloud, rain, snow, frost and mist. The literal meaning of the Greek meteoros is something raised up, but the modern interpretation of the derivation, meteorology, is used to describe all types of weather, however it occurs.

Aristotle would probably approve of the way weather has been classified over the years, in more recent times the inspiration of Francis Beaufort in 1805 perhaps made the greatest contribution with his wind scale. Nowadays, with particular relevance to air travel, meteorologists have classified droplet sizes to differentiate between rain and drizzle. Distances of visibility determine the classification of mist or fog and precise heights decide whether a cloud is low (strato), medium (alto) or high (cirro). Even the amount of cloud cover is broken down and normally described in eighths. All this can be baffling to a normal observer but for the modern pilot it is essential knowledge. Understanding the causes and results of the Earth's weather can make the difference between life and death. To others it can be the difference in being wet or dry on the way to the car park!

Many excellent books have been written about the weather, usually by meteorologists or pilots. The *Air Pilot's Practical & Theoretical Weather Manual* has been created from the pooled knowledge of pilots and meteorologists to assist flight planning for visual or instrument flights by a study of the weather from the aspects affecting any flight.

The information does go into depth, up to, and in some cases beyond the level required for instrument rated pilots but it deliberately avoids deep theory about subjects that have no real practical application to pilots. The book has been conceived to be simple to use by any pilot and enable a greater understanding of the causes and results of the UK and Europe's variable weather.

For all flights, business or pleasure, the main decision is, do I go or don't I? If I go, what is the worst weather I can expect and why? By breaking down each aspect of the British weather, the manual explains in simple terms the causes and effects of weather changes. It clarifies the theory of air masses, highs, lows and fronts and then puts this into the perspective of actual weather in comparison with the charts, tables, METARS (meteorological aerodrome reports of actual weather) and TAFS (terminal aerodrome forecasts) used for flight planning. By including examples of actual weather on specific days it explains how the forecast was made and why, sometimes, the expected results did not appear.

Forecasting is an inexact science, but for flights within the UK and Europe no pilot has an excuse for meeting *unexpected weather* if the easily obtained meteorological information has been studied and understood. This book will ensure you know what is happening to the weather around you.

Chapter 1
The Earth

The Earth is surrounded by layers of atmosphere. At various heights these layers are given names to enable their properties to be categorised. The layer nearest the Earth is the troposphere. This is surrounded by the stratosphere. The two further layers are the mesosphere and ionosphere but all the Earth's weather is contained within the first two layers.

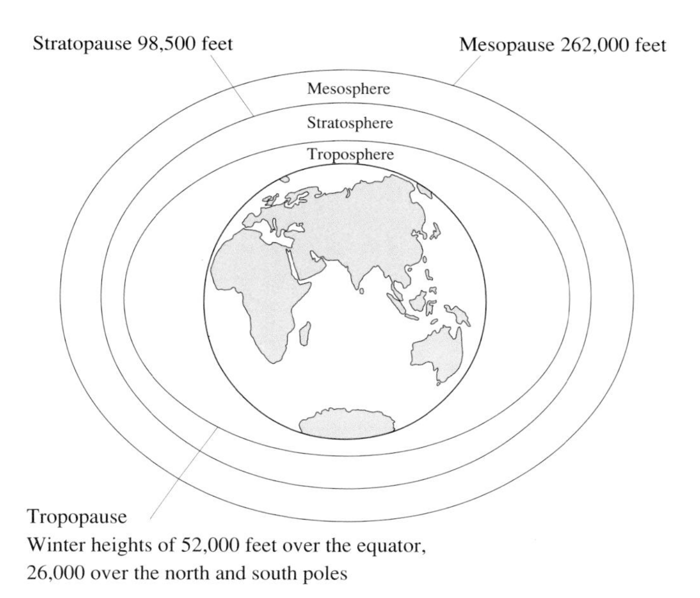

Figure 1.1 The layers of atmosphere surrounding the Earth. The widths are not to scale.

The outer limit of the troposphere is known as the tropopause and all the weather described in this book will be below this layer. Only the most active and rare storms have the power to break through the tropopause and into the stratosphere. The height of the tropopause changes with the seasons over which it lies. The diagram above shows winter heights but these increase slightly in the summer. It is also twice as high over the equator as it is over the poles. This is due simply to the fact that warm air expands.

This difference is caused by the curvature and composition of the Earth in the areas away from the equator. At the equator the Earth is affected by the full power of the Sun's rays. These heat the surface that then warms the air above it, causing expansion. The surface of the poles, where the Sun only just rises above the horizon, receives hardly any surface warming, even during the summer. Many rays that do make contact are reflected back by snow, ice and water, further reducing their heating effect.

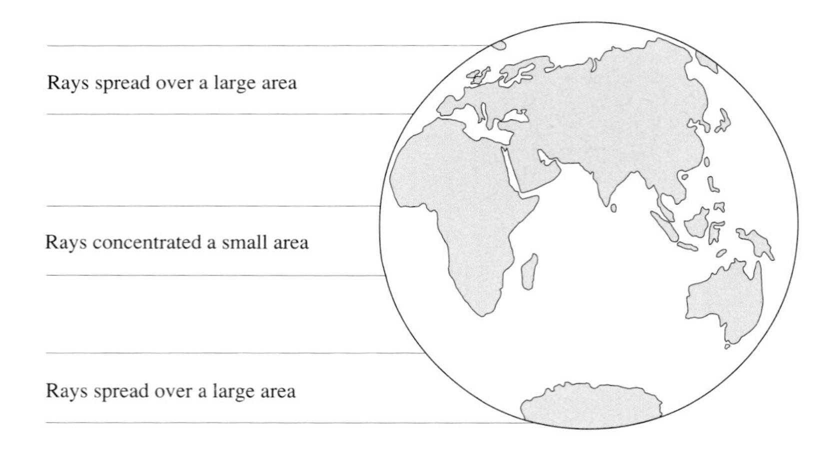

Figure 1.2 A specific amount of the Sun's heat is spread over a larger surface area at the Poles.

As air warms it expands, both outwards and upwards. This causes an increase in the height of the tropopause. The weight of the air presses down on the air below, causing a comparatively high pressure within the warm mass and a maximum pressure at the Earth's surface. Cold air is dense, taking up much less space. The more it cools, the more it contracts. Consequently the tropopause is lower over a cold air mass and, as a result, less air is pressing down on the air below it. The differences between the cold and warm areas within the troposphere are the basic cause of the Earth's weather systems moving as the opposing temperatures and pressures attempt to equalise. Although temperatures and pressures at the surface vary from day to day, the change with height is predictable. At lower levels the temperature will change differently with height dependent on whether the air is dry or damp. At a height of 5 – 10,000 feet, air has a predictable lapse rate (drop per 1,000 feet) of around 2°C per 1,000 feet. This continues up to around 40,000 feet (an average tropopause height) where it falls to -56.5°C until about 70,000 feet. After that it starts to increase. This lapse rate is always the same but the starting point temperature, at the Earth's surface, varies.

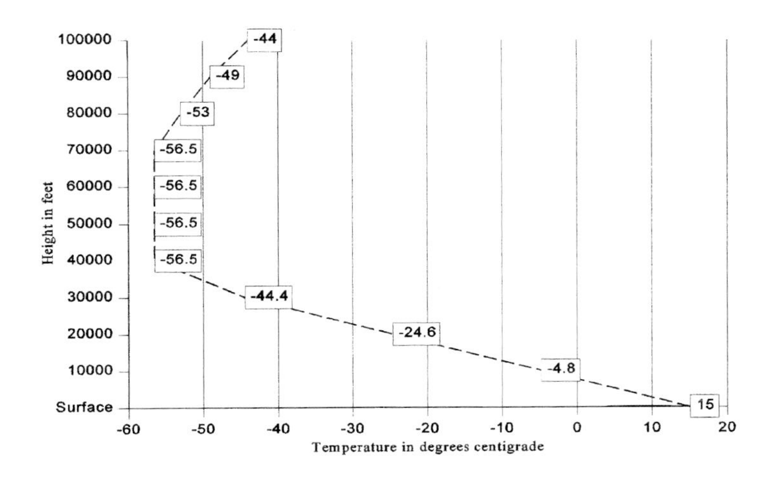

Figure 1.3 Temperature reduction with height.

The pressure lapse rate is also predictable. This is a very useful property easily displayed by the altimeter and vertical speed indicator. Figure 1.4 shows the pressure lapse rate which is one millibar for each 27 feet up to around 3,000 feet. Up to 10,000 feet this increases to one millibar for each 30 feet. After this, the height per millibar slowly increases until the tropopause (averaged at 40,000 feet). Above this you need to climb 200 feet just to get a one millibar drop.

As with temperature, although the lapse rates are predictable, the starting place will be different. Pressure at the surface may be lower than 950 millibars or higher than 1050 millibars. The change with height will always be the same. These differences at the surface, and throughout their height, provide for great activity as the masses attempt to equalise.

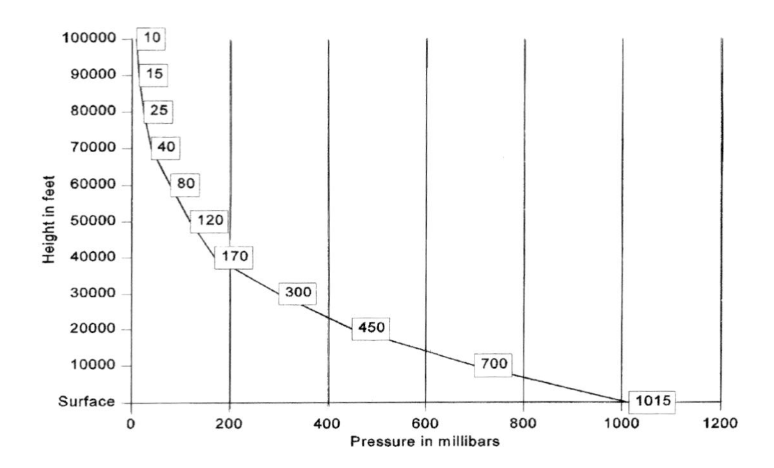

Figure 1.4 Pressure reduction with height

Chapter 2

Major Influences on the UK's Weather

High and Low Pressure Systems

Over the UK, at any particular time, lie high or low pressure areas or sometimes a combination of both. These areas are constantly on the move and, dependent on their origins and circulatory system, dictate what variation of weather conditions we will experience on the ground and in the air. To show graphically where the centres and areas of high and low pressure lie, a line called an isobar is used. An isobar is a line joining points of equal pressure. Surface pressure is measured by weather stations. They convert their readings to the sea level equivalent by using the local atmospheric conditions resulting in a pressure value known as the QFF. The QFF values are passed to a central office where the synoptic, or comprehensive view, surface pressure charts are produced. From these charts we can see at a glance where the pressure systems lie and, by the distance apart that the lines are drawn, what the wind strength will be.

The movement of air masses from various parts of the world affect the UK in different ways. Figure 2.1 shows the names and sources of the main air masses. Obviously air systems do not always approach in straight lines and from the exact directions shown; in reality they mix and modify a bit. However, their general approach direction will give a good indication of what to expect.

By definition an air mass is a large quantity of air that is allowed to remain stationary for several days. It takes on the characteristics of its source region with uniform temperature and humidity. These masses eventually move away from their source regions and those that travel towards the UK and Europe are affected by the land or sea mass over which they journey.

Specific names describe the source of air masses and their

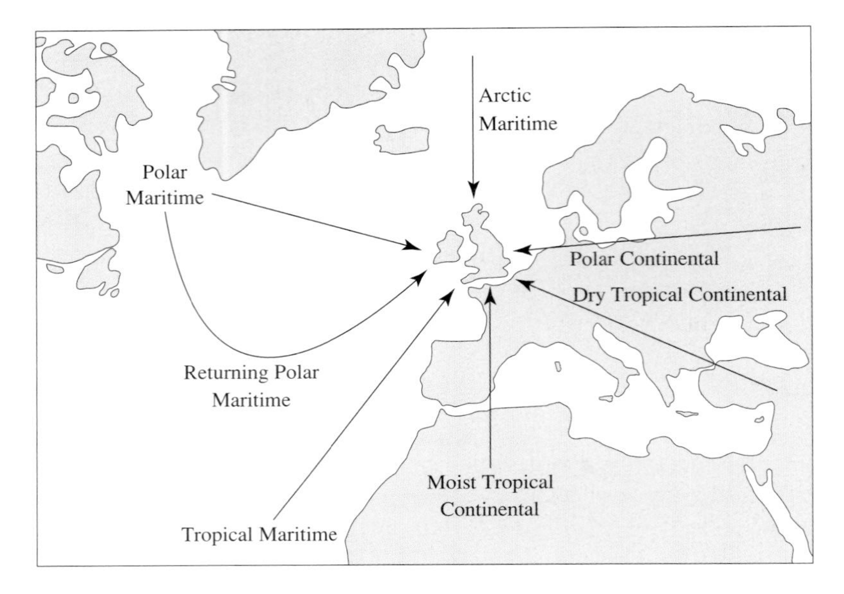

Figure 2.1 The main source regions of air masses affecting the UK.

moisture content. Apart from a temperature change, the stability and moisture content of an air mass are the main causes of changeable weather. If a mass is warm and cools on its approach and arrival over the UK it will become more stable and not be prone to lifting, remaining stable and predictable. If however, a cold mass is caused to warm, the air lifts, cools adiabatically with height, and produces active clouds and weather.

The term adiabatic describes a change of temperature of a mass of air purely by pressure. Air forced to rise will experience a reduction in pressure permitting expansion. The temperature of the air consequently drops. A temperature drop caused solely by the reduction in pressure is known as adiabatic cooling. Where the air temperature increases solely due to increased pressure, i.e. compression, it is known as adiabatic heating. This effect can be proved practically with a bicycle pump that becomes hot when used to compress air.

The extent of adiabatic cooling is determined by the amount of lifting. A large area of stratus cloud will signify stable air with limited lift. The ultimate unstable air, the thunderstorm, can result in air from the surface mixing with that at 40,000 feet with up and down drafts of 5,000 feet a minute.

Air Masses affecting the UK

Arctic Maritime is stable, cold, moist air, which warms, rises, and becomes very unstable on its approach to the UK. Heavy rain or snow showers are common over the sea and windward coasts. As it gradually becomes less moist and cooler overland the cloud and showers die out. The resultant weather is cold and clear with good visibility.

Polar Maritime is cold, stable, moist air, bringing rain showers with cumulus and cumulonimbus resulting in the possibility of thunderstorms as it warms, becomes unstable and more humid. Visibility is generally good but in winter radiation fog can form under clear skies and, if sufficiently dense, may remain for long periods.

Returning Polar Maritime is polar maritime air that travels past the UK and then returns northwards. Its moisture content depends on how far the air has travelled south. On reaching the UK, and if it has travelled far enough south to warm up, it will give moist, foggy weather and resemble tropical maritime air as it cools and stabilises. If its journey south was limited, it will result in weather similar to Polar Maritime air.

Tropical Maritime is, as its name suggests, warm moist air. It brings poor visibility with stratus and stratocumulus. As it cools it becomes more stable often resulting in clear skies above a solid stratus layer. Below, there may be sea and hill fog with haze at night. Precipitation is at worst drizzle. In summer stratus cloud may form at night with a haze layer trapped underneath. This usually breaks up during the day into stratocumulus and cumulus.

You'll find the word precipitation used frequently throughout this book, in meteorological terms it is used to describe any form of water reaching the ground whether it is rain, snow or hail (for a full list of types of precipitation see chapter 14).

Polar Continental is stable, very cold, dry air. It brings hazy visibility but usually clear skies. However if its passage was over the North Sea the increase in moisture will result in stratocumulus and cumulus cloud giving coastal showers to the East.

Finally, Tropical Continental which in summer usually brings good sunbathing weather for those on the ground and can result in heatwave conditions. It is hot, dry stable air bringing clear skies in summer, fine and mild weather in winter. Visibility in any season is reduced by haze. If the air has a more southerly source, it will have travelled over the Mediterranean Sea and Bay of Biscay. Being fundamentally dry it will absorb moisture as it crosses, which, on arrival over the UK, will result in air of maritime characteristics.

Synoptic Weather Observations

There are about five thousand weather stations around the world that regularly report their current and recent weather to regional headquarters. These reports are called synoptic weather observations and lead to the preparation of synoptic charts. On these, each station's weather is shown by meteorological station circle codes. All other charts are then prepared from the synoptic charts.

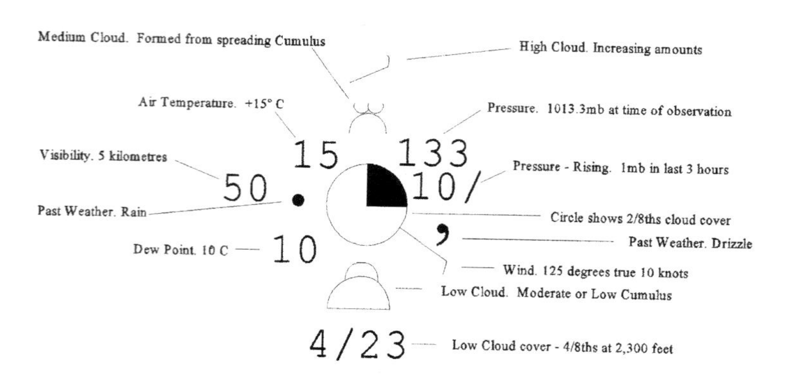

Figure 2.2 A typical station circle.

SURFACE OBSERVATION CODE [FM12-VIII Ext. SYNOP and FM13-VIII Ext. SHIP]

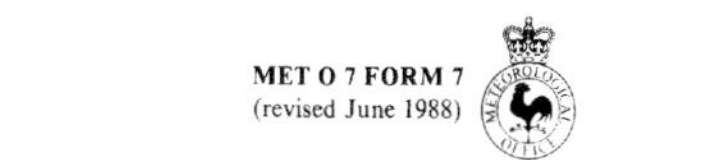

MET O 7 FORM 7
(revised June 1988)

Colour code Black = elements plotted in black: Red = elements plotted in red: Blue = group indicators/optional and non-plotted groups
[Plotting models — to be used in conjunction with Handbook of Weather Messages Parts II and III — Met.O.920b and c]

Section 0 MMMM (D....D)** or (A b n n n)** YYGGi (IIiii)* (99L L L Q L L L L)** [* — used in FM12-SYNOP : ** — used in FM13-SHIP]

Section 1 i i hVV Nddff 00fff 1s TTT 2s T T T 3P P P P {4PPPP or 4a hhh} 5 appp 6RRRt {7wwW W or 7w w //} 8N C C C [Note: i = 2 or 5 wwW W omitted:
i = 3 or 6 wwW W plotted as //: i = 1 or 4 and 7-group is missing wwW W should be plotted as //. Temperatures are plotted to nearest whole degree. Last three figures only of pressure group are plotted]

Section 2 222 D v 0s T T T 1 P P H H 2 P P H H 3 d d d d 4 P P H H 5 P P H H 6I E E R 70H H H ICE + [Plain language or c S b D z]

Section 3 333 1s T T T 2s T T T 3Es T T 4E'sss 8 N C h h 9SpSps s

Section 5 555 1V f'f' 2s T T T

REDUCED SYNOP (SYRED) [Symbols/figures plotted as in adjacent model. The 6- and 8-groups in Sections 1 and 3 respectively are reported only by designated stations]

Section 0 As in Main Code
Section 1 i i hVV Nddff 1s TTT 2s T T T 6RRRt 7wwW W 8N C C C
Section 3 333 1s T T T 2s T T T 3Es T T 4E'sss 8 N Ch h 9SpSps s
Section 5 555 1V f'f' 2s T T T

ABBREVIATED/REDUCED SHIP [Symbols/figures plotted as in adjacent model]

Section 0 As in Main Code
Section 1 i i hVV Nddff 1s TTT 4PPPP 7wwW W 8N C C C
Section 2 222 D v 0s T T T 6I E E R ICE + [Plain language or c S b D z]
[In reduced form, solidi indicate data which are not reported, e.g. {1s TT// 4PPP//}]

FM13-SHIP Q 1 = Longitude East; 7 = Longitude West (Northern hemisphere)
3 = Longitude East; 5 = Longitude West (Southern hemisphere)

ww = 07, 93 to 95 and 97. The solidus separates alternative symbols.
Missing wind data are indicated thus:
Missing wind speed
Wind direction variable
DF Missing wind speed and direction
Wind feathers face anti-clockwise in the southern hemisphere.

Automatic stations are indicated by plotting an equilateral triangle around the station circle so that the apex of the triangle points towards the position of the medium cloud symbol i.e.
When surface wind is calm a circle is plotted outside the triangle i.e.

d d or d d plotted as a wavy black line with an arrow head directed away from the source
e.g. 323// 40806 0806 d d missing
d d = 99 is plotted d d = 00 is plotted

When space is limited C N/h h and C N/h may be plotted N C h h or N C

Printed in the UK for HMSO. Dd 8068771 9/88 C20 9385 4060

Figure 2.3 Station Circle Decode – Part 1

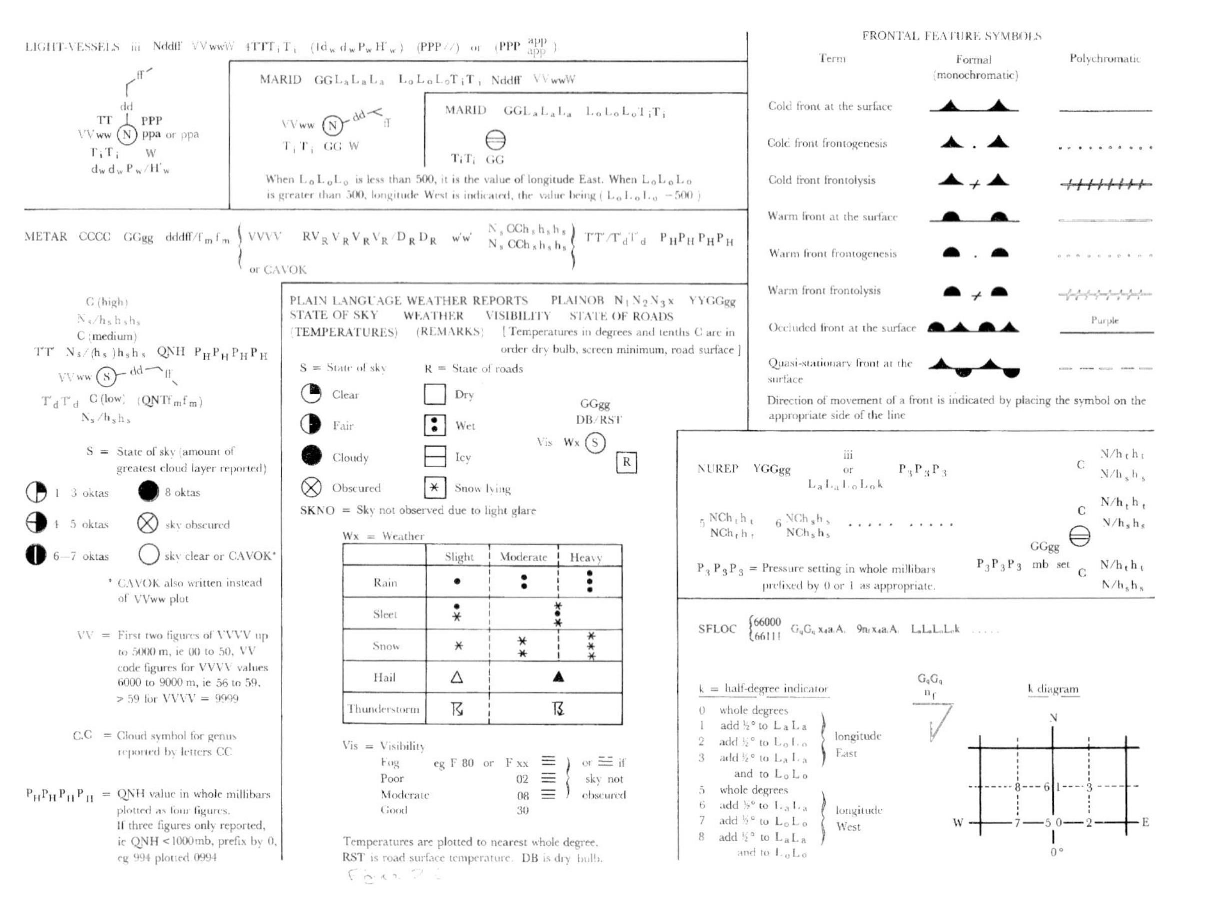

Figure 2.4 Station Circle Decode – Part 2

CHAPTER 3

DEPRESSIONS

A depression is an area of low pressure, also known as a low. If elongated areas form away from the main centre they are called troughs. In the northern hemisphere the wind always blows anticlockwise around a low pressure system due to the geostrophic or, as named after its discoverer, the Coriolis Effect. This is an effect caused by the rotation of the Earth and is explained further in Chapter 16. In the southern hemisphere the reverse applies (i.e. the wind blows clockwise). Most depressions affecting the UK develop from instability in the polar front, but can form in other ways.

Other causes of atmospheric depressions . . .

Localised depressions, known as lee or orographic depressions, occur on the leeward side of mountain ranges. Moving air finds it difficult to pass over mountains, and even fronts may be held up temporarily. The lee depressions are the result of a low pressure area forming in the lee of the mountain. This area is affected by the Coriolis Effect that causes anticlockwise winds (in the northern hemisphere) to form and rotate around the centre of low pressure. The wind is referred to as cyclonic. These low pressure areas are usually temporary and localised but occasionally grow to develop a front.

Thermal depressions form when a land mass becomes heated causing the air above it to rise. The reduction in pressure at the surface pulls in cooler air, usually from the sea. The high altitude pressure of the warm area will be higher than that around it causing a flow away to surrounding areas. The Coriolis Effect force then affects the flow and the wind becomes cyclonic. Again, in the

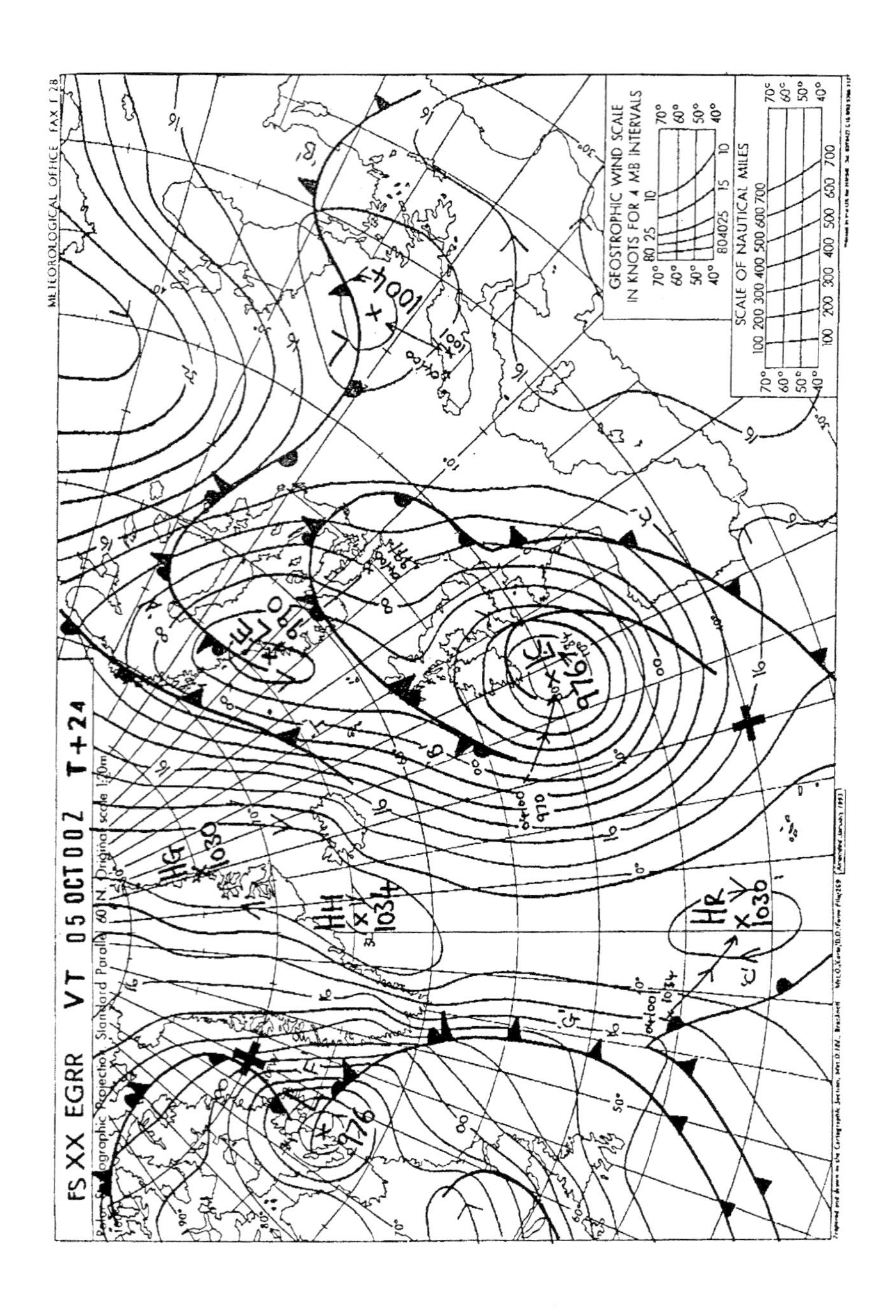
FS XX EGRR VT 05 OCT 00Z T+24
METEOROLOGICAL OFFICE FAX I 28
GEOSTROPHIC WIND SCALE
IN KNOTS FOR 4 MB INTERVALS
SCALE OF NAUTICAL MILES
HG
1030
HH
1034
HR
1030
976
1004
970

northern hemisphere, this means anticlockwise but in the southern hemisphere, clockwise. The resultant thermal depression at the surface can trigger localised clouds and rain when areas around it are clear.

Polar depressions occur in winter when very cold polar air blows into latitudes where the sea is much warmer. They are not as strong as the thermal land lows but as the upper air tends to be so comparatively cold the bad weather produced is usually severe and can last for several days.

Secondary depressions occasionally form at the point of an occlusion and on the trailing edge of a weakening front. They are small areas of low pressure next to a larger depression and within its circulation. These usually form as the primary depression is filling or becoming inactive and so effectively prolong the bad weather. They bring a low cloud base and continuous rain or snow. In summer, thunderstorms are commonly accompanied by gale force winds changing rapidly in strength and direction.

Figure 3.1 (opposite) A surface analysis chart showing a low pressure system dominating the UK. The anticlockwise airflow is dragging Arctic Maritime air down from the polar regions and dragging it back up as returning Polar Maritime air. This results in a very moist stable air bringing stratocumulus and cumulus. Because of the warming caused by its journey south it becomes unstable giving heavy showers on the windward coasts and moist, foggy weather with poor visibility. Not nice visual flying conditions by any means. The closely packed isobars initially produced winds of up to 40 knots and those to the left of the low's centre resulted in winds of up to 80 knots as the system passed west to east over the UK.

Chapter 4

Anticyclones

Anticyclones are areas of high pressure, usually known simply as highs. A high pressure area extending away from the centre is called a ridge. In the northern hemisphere the wind always blows clockwise around a high pressure system due to the Coriolis Effect; in the southern hemisphere the reverse applies.

Anticyclones are formed when an air mass is subject to divergence and moves away from an area that is then known as the centre of pressure. This results in the upper air within the area of the anticyclone descending towards the surface. Anticyclones can be warm or cold. In a cold anticyclone air temperatures near the surface are relatively low resulting in a high air density; this will cause the surface winds to be anticyclonic. At altitude the pressure will be low and cyclonic. Wind direction will vary little in strength and can even reverse in direction between the surface and 20,000 feet.

A warm anticyclone will result in high pressure at altitude with the wind direction and strength varying very little throughout the system. There is generally no significant weather associated with an anticyclone. In the UK it is usually signified by a moist stable air mass with low level mist or fog, often with clear skies above. Although ground dwellers will sing the praises of these conditions it can mean that VMC (visual meteorological conditions) flights are not possible due to poor visibility.

Figure 4.1 (opposite) A surface analysis chart showing a high pressure system dominating the UK. The clockwise airflow is circulating various types of air but mainly tropical maritime. This is initially warm, moist and unstable but as it travels north becomes stable due to cooling. In this example the visibility will be poor over the sea and windward coasts with stratus and stratocumulus clouds inland. As the isobars are well spaced there will be little wind and under clear skies frost will occur if the temperature drops to freezing overnight with mist during the day.

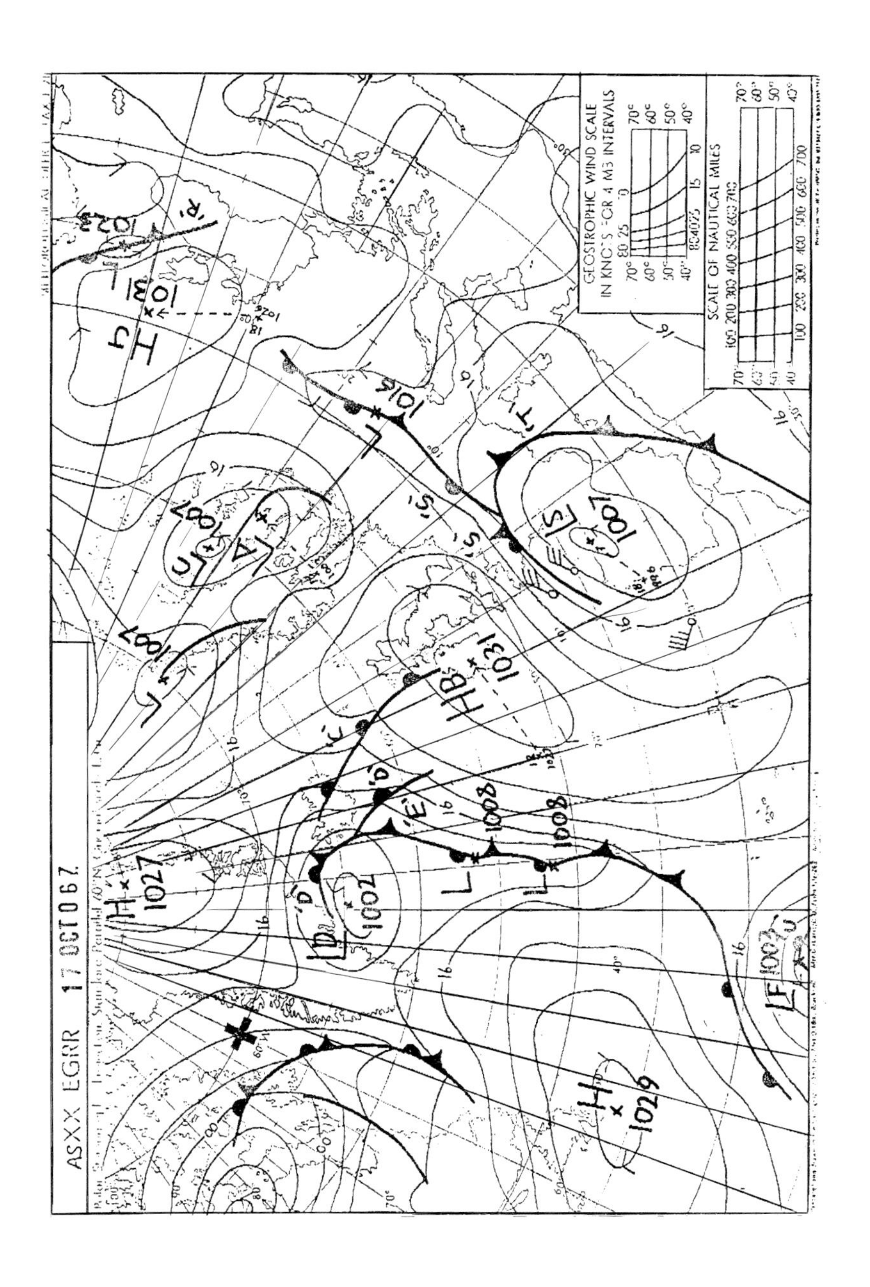
ASXX EGRR 17 OCT 067
GEOSTROPHIC WIND SCALE
IN KNOTS FOR 4 MB INTERVALS
SCALE OF NAUTICAL MILES
H 1027
H 1029
HB 1031
L 1002
L 1007
L 1008
L 1008
L 1016
1002

CHAPTER 5

FRONTS

Front is the term used to describe the line where one classification of air mass ends and another starts. The most marked short period change to the weather comes about by frontal activity. Fronts affecting the UK are mainly caused by a disruption of the polar front. This is the dividing line between the northern polar air and the warmer subtropical southern air. The polar front generally lies between Newfoundland and the north of Scotland in summer and drifts south to lie between Florida and the south-west of England during the winter. A disruption of the polar front will cause a wave to develop. These waves sometimes run along the front without maturing but can often grow into an independent pressure system with a depression at its centre.

If a disruption of the polar front does develop, it will result in two fronts being created, warm and cold. The warm front is always ahead of the cold but moves at a slower speed, typically between one third and half of that of a cold front. As the movement progresses the cold front will catch up with the warm front ahead. The point at which the cold front catches up with the warm front is called an occlusion.

Another type of frontal activity occurs in equatorial regions. This is the area where converging winds either side of the Equator meet to form an inter-tropical front. The temperature difference between the two zones is not great but is enough to develop some convection clouds. Our text will however restrict itself to the frontal activity affecting the UK and Europe.

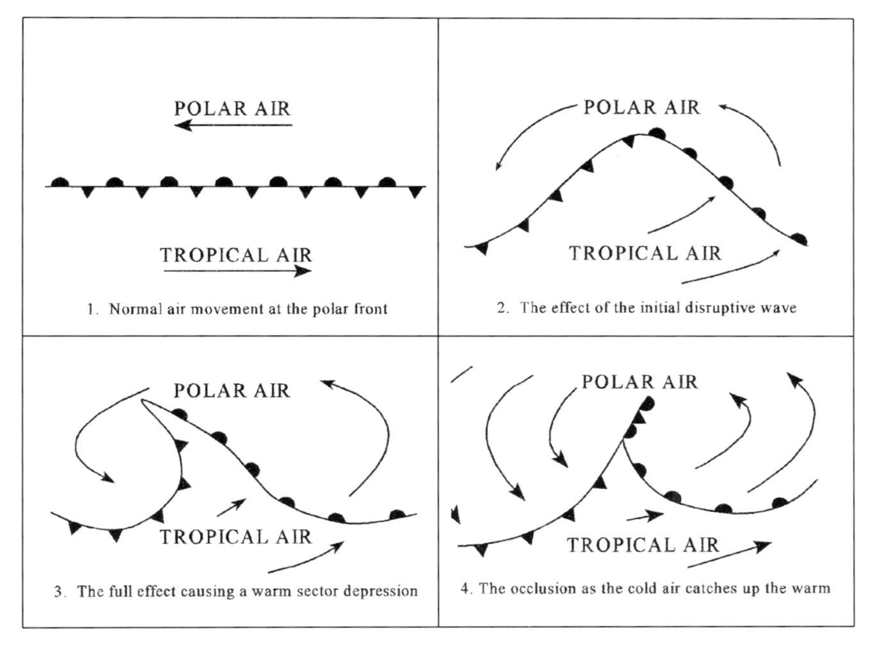

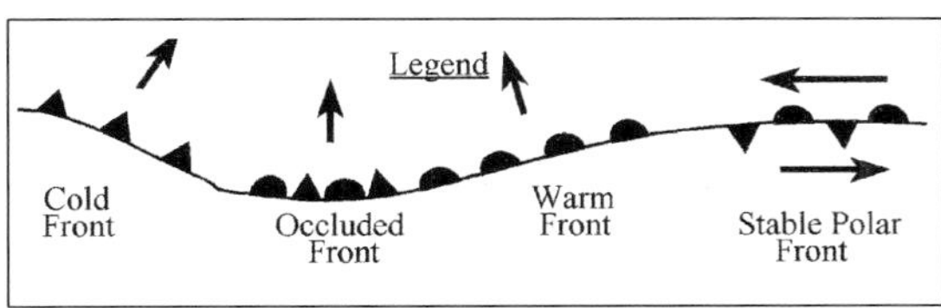

Figure 5.1 Disruption of the Polar Front causing warm, cold and occluded fronts.

Chapter 6

A Warm Front

A warm front is the term given to the ground level boundary between warm air and the cooler air ahead of it. The warm sector, which is the air behind the warm front, is being pushed along by a mass of cold air behind it. As the warm frontal air rises over the cold air ahead, it forms a shallow uphill slope. It is up this slope that the cloud and weather form.

Visual detection of an approaching warm front is simple as several hundred miles downwind of the front the first wisps of ice crystal

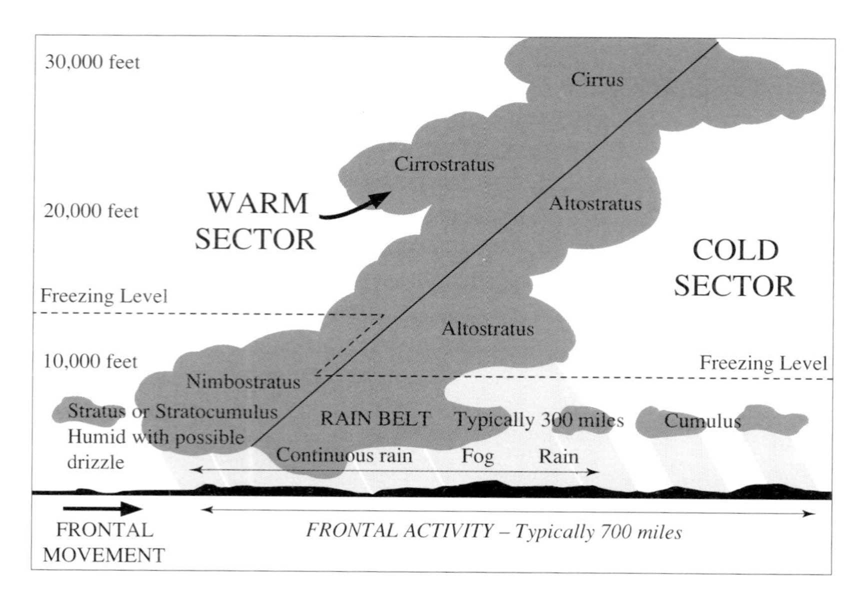

Figure 6.1 A theoretical cross-section of a warm front when observed from the surface. The angle of the rising warm air front has been exaggerated for the purposes of this diagram, an actual angle would be in the region of 1:100.

cloud will become visible from the ground. They are cirrus clouds and will be several miles high. As the front approaches the cirrus is replaced by cirrostratus that eventually thickens to block out any sunshine. The cloud base steadily lowers with a band of altostratus that brings rain or snow. This can be light or heavy dependent on the intensity of the front. It can last for several hours during which time the lowest cloud, nimbostratus, will pass resulting in hill fog and very poor visibility.

Weather charts show a warm front as a black line with equally spaced black semicircles in the direction of movement of the front.

Characteristic	In Advance	In Passing	After Passing
Barometric Pressure	Steady Fall	Steady	Steady
Temperature	Steady or slow rise	Rise	Steady
Cloud Amount	Increasing	Total cover	Decreasing
Cloud Base	Lowering	Hill Fog	Low Cloud Type
Cloud Types	Cirrus, Cirrostratus, Altostratus, Nimbostratus (Approaching in that order) Fractostratus and Fractocumulus	Nimbostratus Fractostratus	Stratus, strato-cumulus. Possible Cirrus
Dewpoint and Relative Humidity (RH)	Rising in precipitation	Rise - RH rising if not saturated	Steady – RH at maximum
Surface Wind	Backs, increasing	Veers, decreasing	Steady
Visibility	Good except in rain or snow	Poor in mist or fog	Poor
Weather	Continuous rain or snow	Rain or snow decreasing or stopping	Drizzle or none

The front will give very predictable changes in advance, in passing, and after passing a fixed ground point, making basic weather predictions simple.

Now we know what actually happens with the passage of a warm front, but how is it going to affect a flight through the front? The barometric pressure will fall. This will happen in the area ahead of the front but be steady within and after it. The cloud coverage will increase as the front becomes closer. If you are flying towards a steadily lowering cloud base causing you to make regular descents to remain VMC (Visual Meteorological Conditions) it is a good bet that you are approaching a warm front and unless you are close to your destination or qualified to fly in IMC (Instrument Meteorological Conditions) you should consider an alternative aerodrome.

Close to the rain belt it is very unlikely that the cloud base will allow a VMC flight as it will usually be at a maximum of a few hundred feet, resulting in fog over hills and high ground. The wind will back and increase, making any flight planned headings obsolete. It is not possible to flight plan accurately for wind headings and strengths near and within a front. As the front passes the wind speed will reduce and veer, again affecting any heading calculations made for an IMC passage. In compensation, the wind strength and direction become steady after the passage of the front.

The dewpoint will rise, maximizing with the passing of the front, and becoming steady afterwards. The dewpoint is the temperature to which air can cool, with no change of pressure, without condensation occurring. In this state the air is saturated and any cooling below this temperature will cause condensation. Condensation is cloud. The closer the dewpoint to the ambient or surrounding temperature the greater the likelihood of mist, fog or cloud forming. The dewpoint and temperature are given on a METAR, a meteorological aerodrome report of the observed weather. Their proximity is a good indicator of the likely visibility.

The visibility is of predominant interest to the VMC pilot, and is usually the deciding point between a flight or a cancellation. With an advancing warm front the visibility is normally good. That is to say that it does not deteriorate. If the visibility is poor before a front passes it will stay poor and become worse at the front. If the visibility is good before the front it will remain clear until the front is met. As the front clears through, the comparatively warm air will

AIRLIFE PUBLISHING LTD.
101 LONGDEN ROAD
SHREWSBURY
SHROPSHIRE SY3 9BR

have a higher moisture content than that it replaced and, as confirmed by the dewpoint approaching that of the ambient temperature, will ensure that visibility remains poor.

After the passage of the front a low base of stratocumulus and stratus cloud cover will remain for a long period but will eventually move past. Warm sectors usually bring poor visibility and nothing is likely to change the situation until colder air arrives.

To the lay person, the weather means how hot, or wet and windy the day is. For the purposes of a meteorological report weather means precipitation. Therefore, aerodrome reports often quote nil weather. This can sound fairly daft unless the context under which it is quoted is understood.

An advancing warm front will bring rain or snow. The fact that it could bring snow may seem a contradiction for a warm front passage until the definition is considered. A warm front is the ground level boundary between warm air and cooler air ahead of it. It is

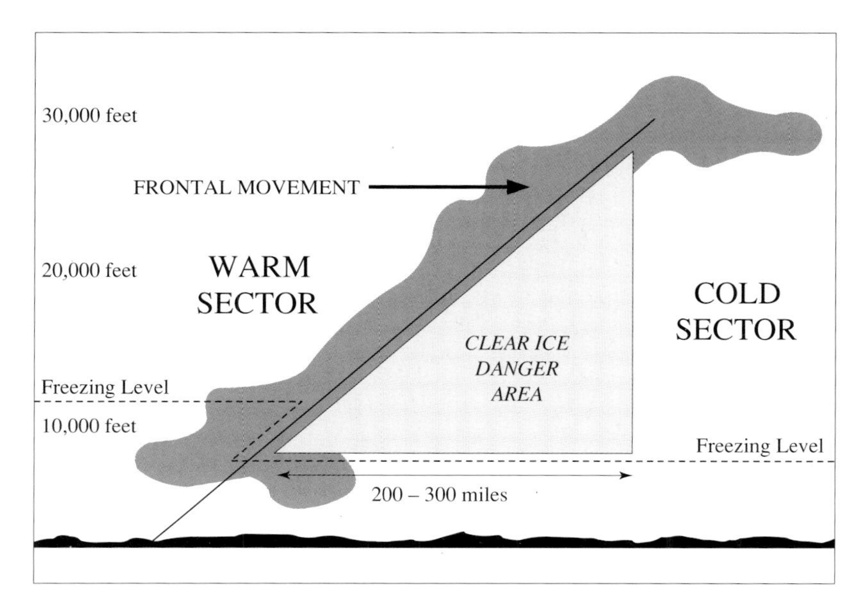

Figure 6.2 A cross-section of a warm front when observed from the surface showing the clear air icing area. This diagram shows the risk area to be around 8,000 feet but this triangle could start from any height. During winter it's possible for the area to be from the surface upwards making the only flight option a 180° turn if icing is encountered.

therefore possible for the air behind a warm front to be at -5°C and the air ahead of it to be colder, so it still qualifies as a warm front.

The simple fact that warm air rises results in the formation of cloud and associated precipitation as the advancing air ascends over the colder air ahead of it. As it rises it cools adiabatically below its dewpoint and forms cloud. As the cloud is forced to rise further, the water droplets will reach a size at which the updrafts cannot support them. They fall to the ground as rain or snow dependent on the temperature.

Airframe icing can be a problem if you are flying in the area in advance of the front even when clear of cloud. If the air at height is at a sub-zero temperature the outer skin of the aircraft will be at the same temperature. If it then encounters rain falling from the high clouds of the advancing warm front above, that rain will have fallen through the sub-zero air and become supercooled. When the droplets encounter an aircraft they will freeze on impact. It goes through a calculable process before each droplet fully freezes but this is covered in more detail in the icing section of this book. This type of icing, known as clear or glaze ice, can form and build very quickly, affecting the control of the aircraft. If an aircraft is not cleared for icing conditions and icing is encountered, it should descend into warmer air if terrain clearance allows and turn away to an area that does not have cloud cover.

CHAPTER 7

A COLD FRONT

A cold front is the name given to the moving surface boundary of cold air and the warm air ahead that it undercuts. This warm air is forced to rise so rapidly that it produces a line of cumulonimbus clouds called a line squall. These produce heavy but short lived rain showers, possibly with hail and thunder. The frontal passage, when observed from a fixed ground point, is unlikely to last more than an hour. A cold front is shown on a weather map as a black line with small triangles in the direction of its path.

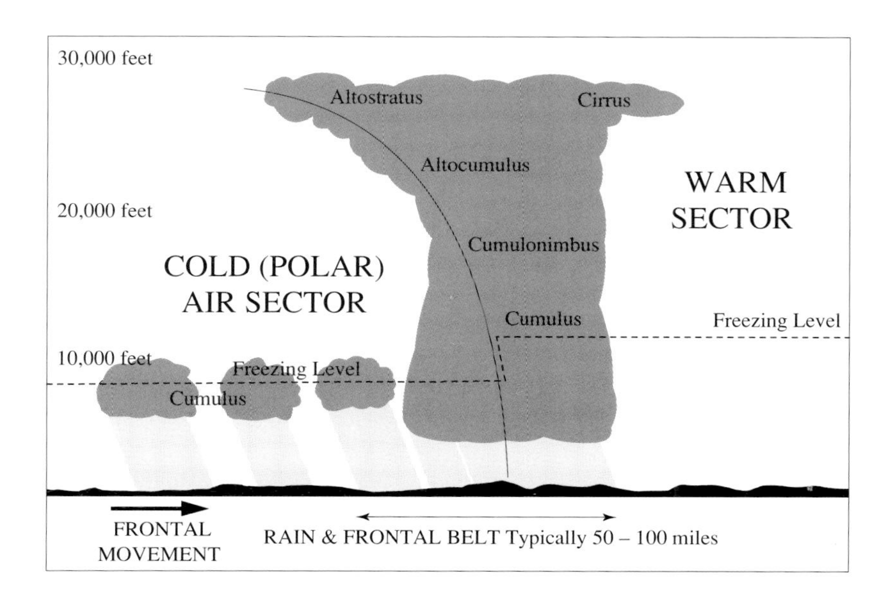

Figure 7.1 A theoretical cross-section of a cold front when observed from the sufrace. The angle of an actual front would be in the region of 1:50.

A cold front will give predictable changes in advance, in passing and after passing a fixed ground point or observer. The changes are tabulated below:

Characteristic	In Advance	In Passing	After Passing
Barometric Pressure	Sudden fall	Sudden rise	Steady or slow rise
Temperature	Steady falling in Pre-frontal rain	Sudden fall	Steady
Cloud Amount **Cloud Base**	None Low	Increase Very low	Decrease Rapid rise
Cloud Types	Stratus or Stratocumulus, Altocumulus, Altostratus then Cumulonimbus	Cumulus, Cumulonimbus, fractostratus, Nimbostratus	Altostratus, Altocumulus, then Cumulus & Cumulonimbus
Dewpoint and Relative Humidity (RH)	Steady – RH high in precipitation	sudden fall – RH high in precipitation	steady – RH falls rapidly as precipitation ceases, variable in showers
Surface Wind	Backs, Increases & Becomes Squally	Sudden Veer	Steady or Veers
Visibility	Misty, Foggy	Poor in rain or snow	Very Good except in snow showers
Weather	Rain , possible thunder	heavy Rain, snow, hail & Thunder	heavy rain or snow. Then fine with Showers later

Figure 7.2 (opposite) A section of a surface analysis chart showing the change of wind direction associated with the passing of a cold front.

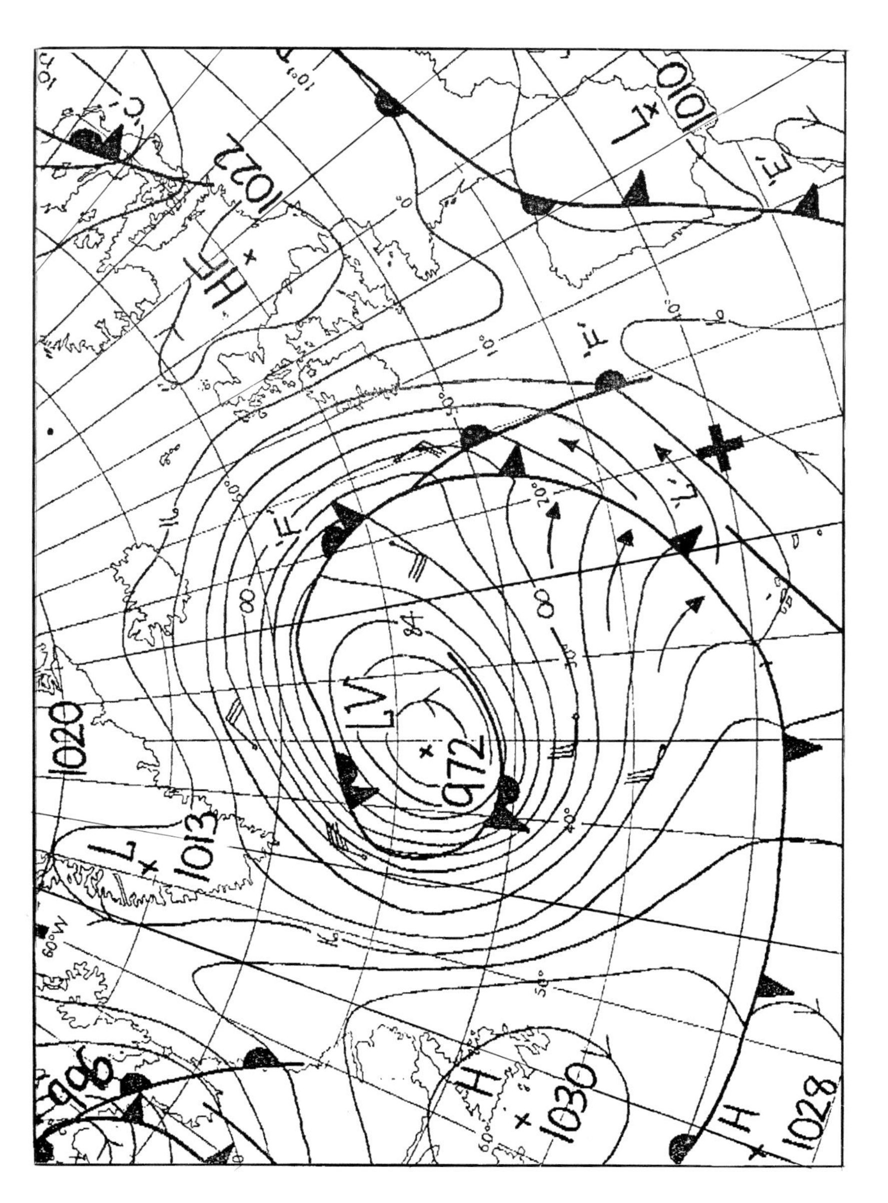

Figure 7.2

As with a warm front any flight through a cold front will be in IMC. It is unlikely that a VFR (Visual Flight Rules) flight could be made under the front as although the cloud base may be high enough for terrain clearance the visibility in rain will be below minima. As this rain belt is typically 50 to 100 miles wide it is a safer bet to wait for it to pass and hope that the usually excellent post-front visibility is good enough to allow the flight to get airborne.

For those on the ground observations of actual changes can be mildly interesting. For those in the air they become important flight safety features. The barometric pressure makes a rapid drop ahead of the front, the rapidity being due to the steep gradient of the front that will cause the altimeter to over-read unless reset, with obvious safety problems. As the front passes a rise in pressure will occur as rapidly as it fell, becoming steady or slowly continuing to rise, dependent on the properties of the cold air behind the front.

The cloud amount in advance of the front does not change until the great column of cloud formed by the rising warm air of the pre-frontal belt arrives. The cloud base may not suggest a great change when observed from the ground if a layer of stratocumulus or stratus already fills the warm sector. The depth of the cloud will change from perhaps a few hundred feet to around 25,000 feet as the front is met. The cloud base is usually quite level but within the rain belt below the main body of the front the rain is likely to be so heavy that visibility is reduced to that of flight in cloud.

As the front passes the lower levels of cloud will break up to give broken cumulus accompanied by showers with altocumulus and altostratus above. The visibility after the passing of a cold front is the great bonus. Behind the front the air has a much lower humidity and, apart from in the odd shower, visibility should be excellent.

The surface wind backs before the front and suddenly veers as it passes. Refer to the surface analysis chart at Figure 7.2 and, bearing in mind that the wind direction flows parallel to the isobars, it can be seen why this change occurs. Again reference to this chart illustrates that after passing, the wind speed and direction will be comparatively steady veering only a little.

Chapter 8
Occlusions

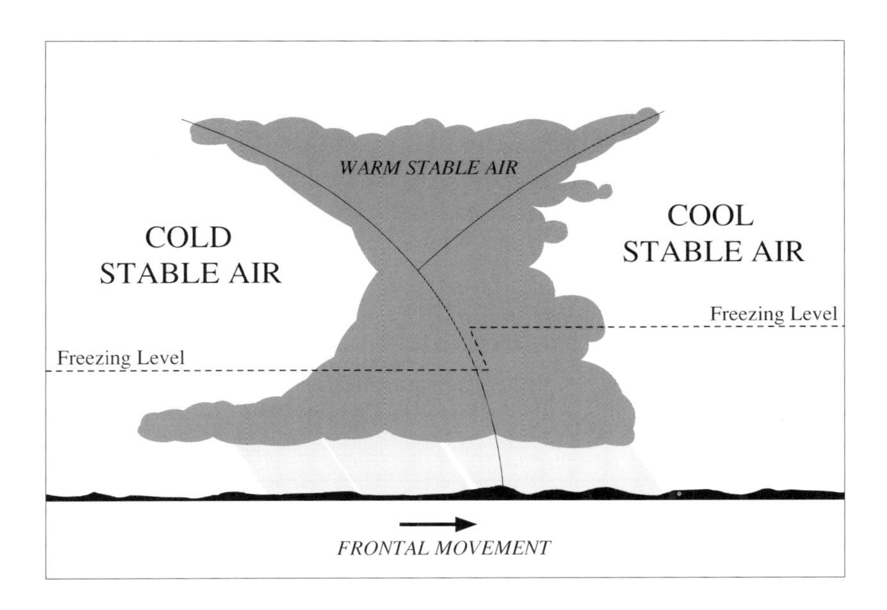

Figure 8.1 The cold front occlusion shown above is of a stable character. This would tend to obscure the line of the front to a ground observer and give a uniform cloud formation throughout the occluded area. Occlusions of this type tend to linger until the low fills. Poor visibility would be expected between the ground and the cloud base with light rain and drizzle. Icing would be moderate with light winds and little turbulence.

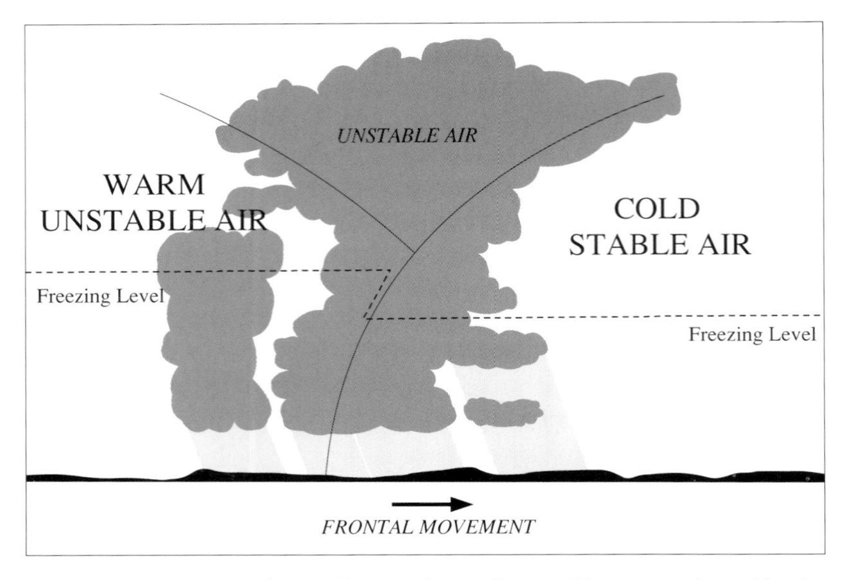

Figure 8.2 The type of warm front occlusion favoured by meteorological books and training manuals. This type is most common in summer and gives rise to thunderstorm and massive vertical cumulus cloud formations as the warm air rises rapidly over the cold air ahead. The visibility and cloud base should only be of academic interest as flight in any area likely to contain thunderstorms is at best foolhardly. This type of occlusion is usually fast moving and can clear through within a few hours.

As mentioned earlier, as a cold front travels faster than a warm front, a time must come when the slower front is overtaken. This area is known as an occlusion, and the front called an occluded front. Most depressions reaching the UK are at least partly occluded, the most common being a cold front occlusion. It is also

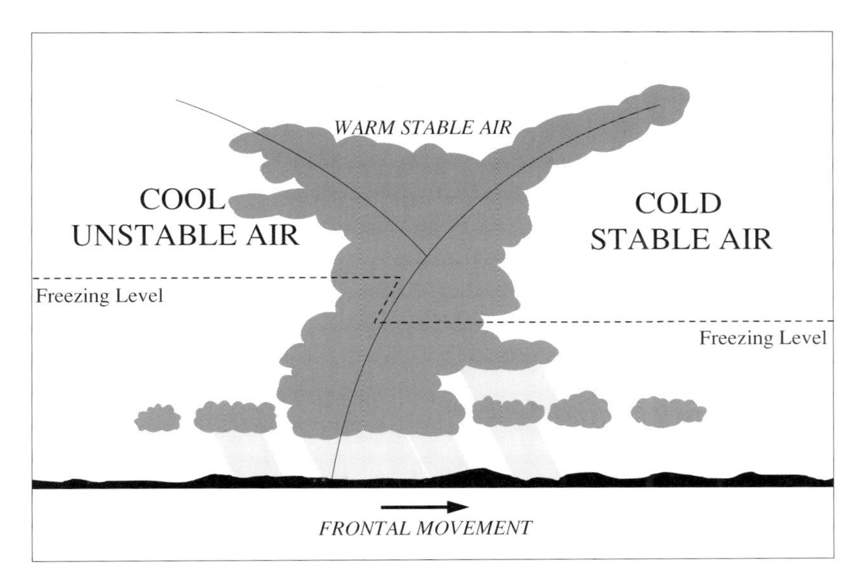

Figure 8.3 Another type of warm front occlusion. The illustration shown above is most common in winter. The cool unstable air rises over the colder air ahead forming turbulent heap clouds. Stratiform clouds form ahead of the front and in the warm sector. Visibility below the cloud may be good but poor in showers. This type of occlusion is usually persistent and slow moving.

possible, under certain circumstances, for a warm front occlusion to form. The defining factor is whether the air behind the occlusion line is warmer or colder than the air in front. An occlusion is shown on a weather chart with black triangles interspaced with black half-circles.

Chapter 9

But in Practice . . .

How do these theoretical air movements relate to practical flight planning? If you are deliberating the conditions, do you really need to know the theory of why things happen? After all you will get Metforms 214 and 215, TAFs & METARs for the route and they will give the exact weather. . . .

So how come when you arrive at the airfield ready to take off, or worse, as you near your destination in flight, the weather is not like you thought it would be? Weather forecasting is based on past performance. Information is collected from weather stations all over the world and the direction of fronts and air masses can be tracked by comparing pressure values and weather conditions as they pass fixed points. Wind and weather at various heights is most important to pilots and this information is gathered from aircraft and by radiosonde. This is an electronic weather station carried up by balloon with equipment that reports the humidity, pressure and temperature of the air at various levels as it passes through them. This data is then transmitted to a ground station. For high level information a rocket is used and the station referred to as a rocket-sonde. The rocket returns to Earth by parachute.

Forecasts are then produced on the basis that if a low pressure system or front has been moving at a steady rate for the last few days it should continue to do so. The position of that weather should, theoretically, be predictable for the next couple of days, or at least hours. However . . . glance at the charts at Figures 9.1 and 9.2. They are both for the same date, same area, and produced by the same Met office. The only difference is that one was generated 72 hours earlier than the other. In the forecast the cold front was expected to be 900 miles off Cornwall by the 15 November and the warm front 600 miles off. As it turned out, the cold front was some 500 miles off and was quickly catching up the warm front that actually lay 450

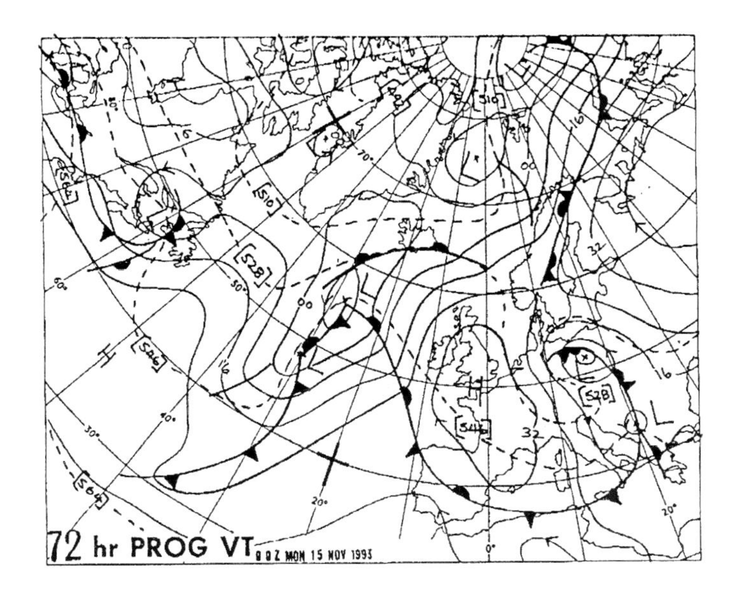

Figures 9.1 and 9.2 The forecast issued on the 12.11.93 for the expected weather position on 15.11.93 together with the actual positions for 15.11.93

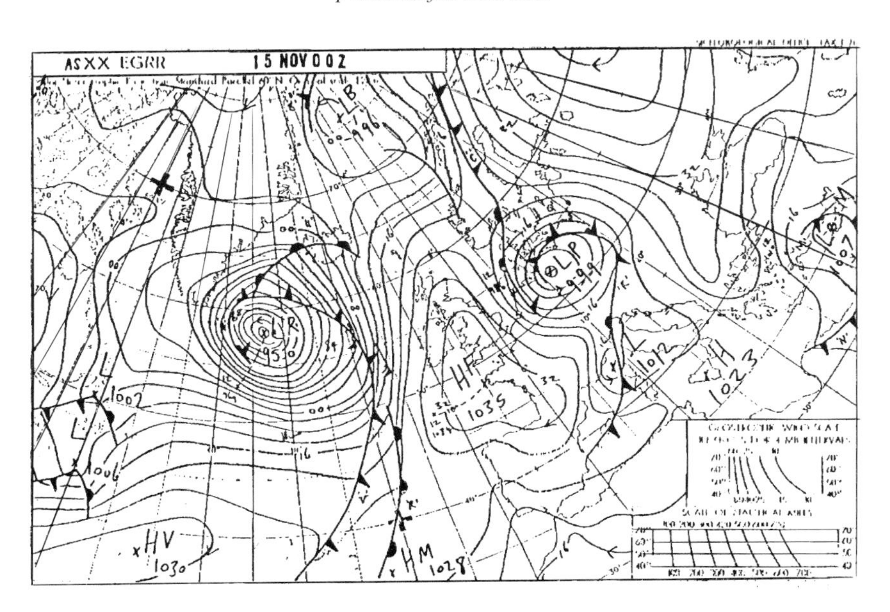

miles off the UK mainland. The reason for this error was that the depression deepened far more than expected, causing an increase in wind speed, pushing the fronts along faster than their past performance had suggested.

The purpose of this explanation is to show how air masses or fronts may not move as expected. We cannot assume that a front or depression will continue to move as it did days or even hours ago. Some phenomena may cause a front to accelerate, stop or even reverse its track. A depression can deepen rapidly or fill with no seemingly logical reason. If this cause cannot be seen and predicted in advance, the forecaster can only plot what is likely to happen given past performance and a bit of guesswork for possible factors. It is of course very easy after the event to explain why any changes occurred!

Chapter 10

Interpreting the Forecasts

The following examples take a specific day and explain why the forecasts and actuals read the way they do and what caused these conditions. With a little practice you could repeat this on any particular day, making your own interpretation of whether the flying conditions suit your ratings and experience.

Example One – Saturday 18 September

The data has been collected via the METFAX system. The Surface Analysis chart at Figure 10.1 shows a high pressure system over the UK with large ridges extending over the centre of Europe and Italy. There is also an active depression, with associated fronts, lying in the mid-Atlantic.

As the winds blow clockwise round a high, the surface wind will be southerly on the western side of the country and light and variable to the east where the centre of the high lies.

The air flow from the ridge and over the UK is a mix of polar maritime and tropical continental. By referring to the text on air masses we can guess that the polar air should result in a stable, cold and moist flow that should bring good visibility, cumulus and possibly cumulonimbus clouds, whereas the tropical continental would bring clear skies mixed with hot, dry stable air and poor visibility. What we cannot work out is how they have mixed over central Europe and which will be most dominant by the time it reaches the UK.

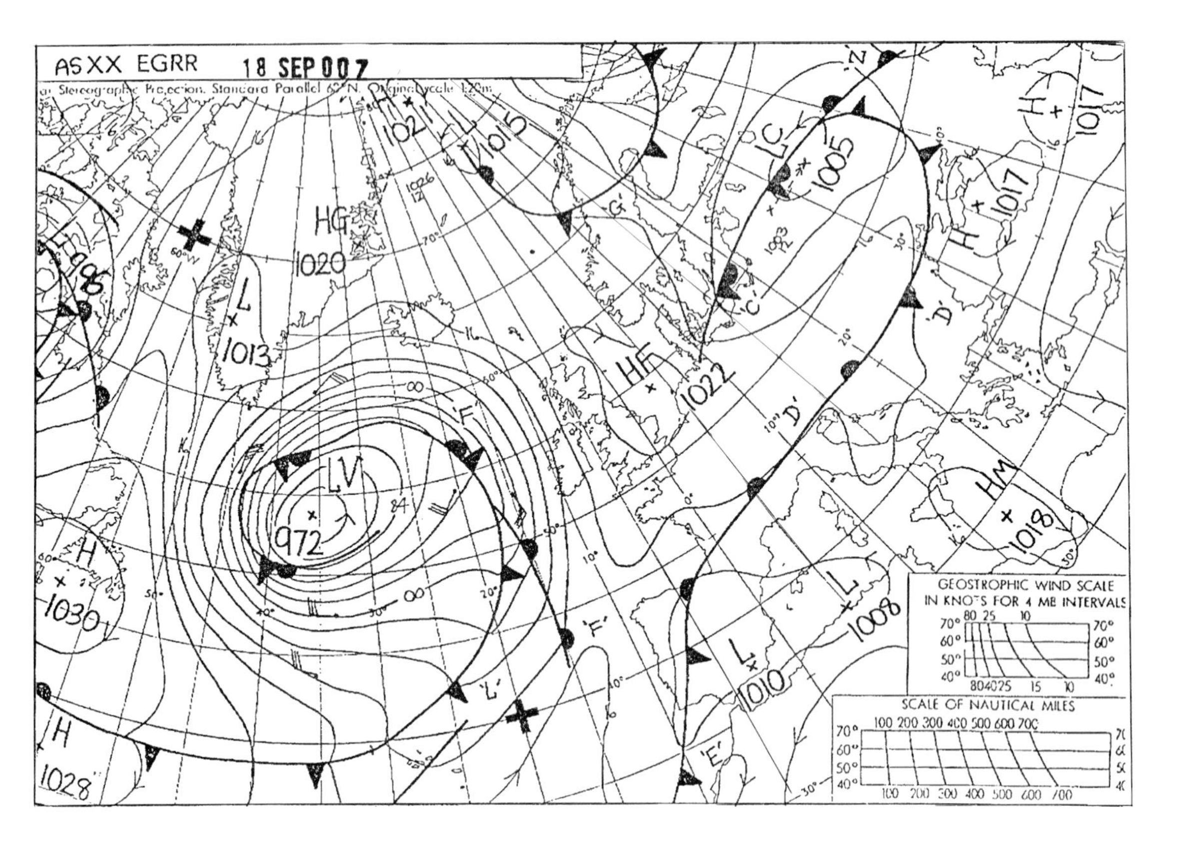

Figure 10.1 Surface analysis chart for 18 September 1993.

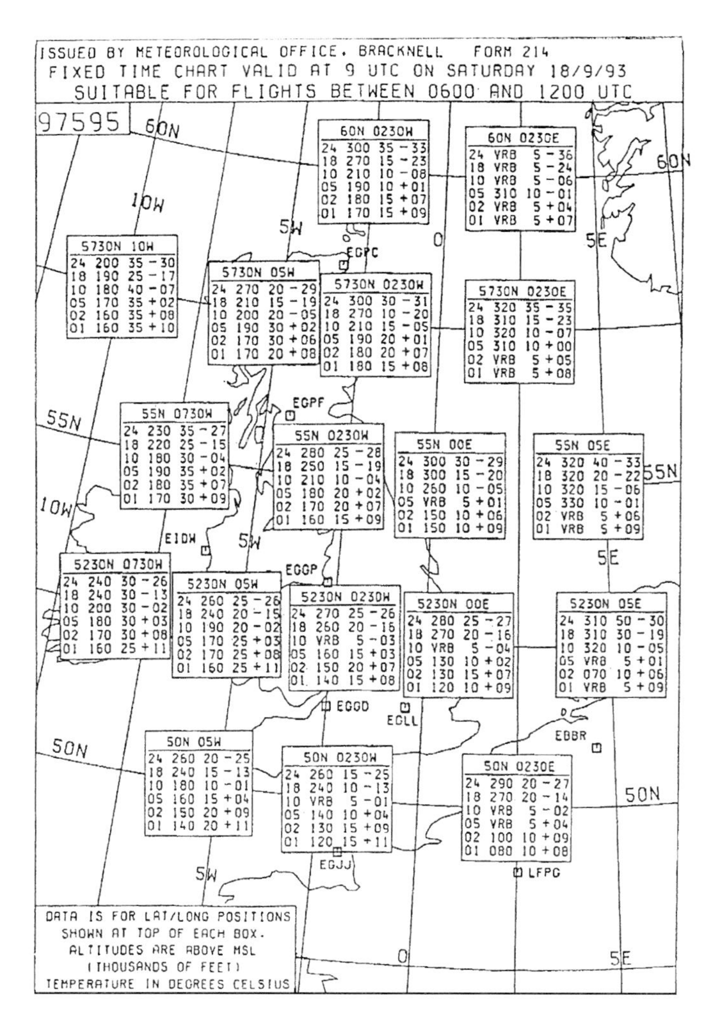

Figure 10.2 Metform 214 valid between 0600Z and 1200Z for 18th September 1993.

The Metform 214

Interpretation of a Metform 214 is relatively straightforward. Each box is given a position of latitude and longitude at the top. To discover the wind and temperature for a given area just look for the nearest box. If your area lies between two boxes simply average out the data. Below the latitude/longitude heading the box always shows the same numbers on the left. These are the heights in thousands of feet: 24,000, 18,000, 10,000, 5,000, 2,000 and 1,000. The next column gives the direction *from* which the wind is blowing to the nearest 10 degrees at each height. The next column shows the wind strength in knots and the final column, the temperature, – denoting a minus, + a plus. So, just to clarify, in Figure 10.2, for the box headed 50N 0230W the wind at 5,000 feet is blowing from 140° at 10 knots and the air temperature is plus 4°C. If you had a flight from Exeter (nearest box 50N 0230W) to Liverpool (nearest box 5230N 0230W) you could average the conditions for the two to give your likely en route wind and temperature.

Position	Height	Wind from	Wind speed	Air temperature
50N 0230W	5,000 feet	140°	10 knots	+ 4
5230N 0230W	5,000 feet	160°	15 knots	+ 3
Average	5,000 feet	150°	12/13 knots	+ 3.5

A glance at the form 214 shows the 1,000 feet wind direction ranging from 120° in the south and 180° in the north. This ties in with the isobars drawn on the Metform 215 (at Figure 10.3) that shows a curving clockwise flow from south to north. The temperature also cross-checks between the forms. On the form 215, freezing levels over the UK are shown in spot temperature boxes, the one just above Liverpool gives the 0° level at 7,000 feet. Looking at the form 214 in the nearest box (5230N 0230W) there is no temperature for 7,000 feet, the nearest is 5,000. We can assume a temperature drop of 2° per 1,000 of altitude and that gives us a 7,000 temperature of -1°C, close enough.

The Metform 215

The Metform 215, UK low level forecast, uses a decode similar to TAFs and METARs, full details of which are given on page 51. The

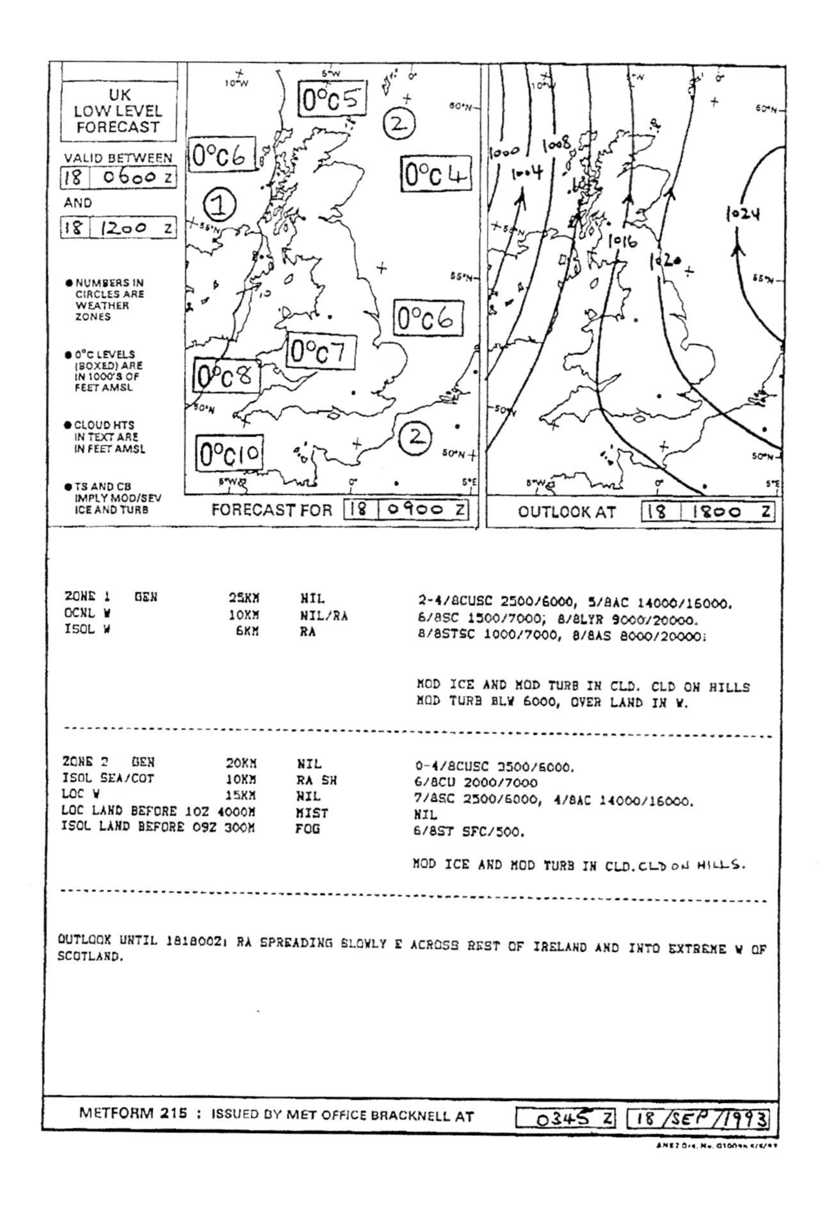

UK LOW LEVEL FORECAST

VALID BETWEEN 18 0600 Z AND 18 1200 Z

- NUMBERS IN CIRCLES ARE WEATHER ZONES
- 0°C LEVELS (BOXED) ARE IN 1000'S OF FEET AMSL
- CLOUD HTS IN TEXT ARE IN FEET AMSL
- TS AND CB IMPLY MOD/SEV ICE AND TURB

FORECAST FOR 18 0900 Z

OUTLOOK AT 18 1800 Z

ZONE 1 GEN	25KM	NIL	2-4/8CUSC 2500/6000, 5/8AC 14000/16000.
OCNL W	10KM	NIL/RA	6/8SC 1500/7000; 8/8LYR 9000/20000.
ISOL W	6KM	RA	8/8STSC 1000/7000, 8/8AS 8000/20000;
			MOD ICE AND MOD TURB IN CLD. CLD ON HILLS MOD TURB BLW 6000, OVER LAND IN W.

ZONE 2 GEN	20KM	NIL	0-4/8CUSC 3500/6000.
ISOL SEA/COT	10KM	RA SH	6/8CU 2000/7000
LOC W	15KM	NIL	7/8SC 2500/6000, 4/8AC 14000/16000.
LOC LAND BEFORE 10Z	4000M	MIST	NIL
ISOL LAND BEFORE 09Z	300M	FOG	6/8ST SFC/500.
			MOD ICE AND MOD TURB IN CLD. CLD ON HILLS.

OUTLOOK UNTIL 181800Z; RA SPREADING SLOWLY E ACROSS REST OF IRELAND AND INTO EXTREME W OF SCOTLAND.

METFORM 215 : ISSUED BY MET OFFICE BRACKNELL AT 0345 Z 18/SEP/1993

Figure 10.3 Metform 215 valid between 0600Z and 1200Z for 18 September 1993.

main difference is that TAF or METAR are just text, whereas the form 215 is presented as a pair of charts and text. Also, the forecast is not based around aerodromes but covers the whole of the UK, broken down when applicable, into zones. The dividing lines for these zones are often prompted by passing fronts that also signal changing weather conditions. For a given zone, variations within the zone will be given, together with the expected cloud tops and an icing and turbulence warning. A decode for Zone 1 on the form 215 at Figure 10.3 is as follows:

Zone	Visiblity	Weather	Cloud
Zone 1 Generally	25 kilometres	Nil	2 to 4 eighths of cumulus and stratocumulus base 2,500 feet, tops 6,000. 5 to 8 eighths of altocumulus base 14,000 feet, tops 16,000
Zone 1 occasionally in the west	10 kilometres	Nil or rain	6 to 8 eighths of stratocumulus base 1,500 feet, tops 7,000. Overcast layers of cloud base 9,000 feet, tops 20,000
Zone 1 isolated patches in the west	6 kilometres	Rain	Overcast stratus and stratocumulus base 1,000 feet, tops 7,000. Overcast altostratus base 8,000, tops 20,000
All of Zone 1	Moderate icing and moderate turbulence in cloud. Cloud on hills. Moderate turbulence below 6,000 feet and over land (not over sea) in the west.		

The chart breaks the country into two zones. Zone 1 is beginning to be affected by the low pressure system moving in from the Atlantic and its accompanying fronts. You can see by the closely spaced isobars over Ireland that the wind will increase and the pressure drop as the low moves in from west to east across the UK. The warm and cold fronts shown on the surface analysis chart will probably be fully occluded by the time they reach Ireland so we can guarantee rain and low cloud is approaching. The air flow prevalent over the UK is southerly, flowing clockwise around the high just centred to the east of the UK. However over Ireland, and, after the hours of this forecast, the wind will still be southerly but dominated by the anticlockwise flow around the low pressure area to the west.

Refer to the form 215 zone 2, this shows that there will be generally less cloud than in zone 1, and with a higher cloud base. In sea and coastal areas there may be isolated patches where the visibility, weather and cloud are the same as that given for occasional in the west for zone 1. Fog is forecast before 0900 hours with reducing visibility to 300 metres. This is expected to improve to mist with visibility improving to 4,000 metres (although technically the criteria for mist ceases if the visibility is in excess of 3000 metres) by 1000 hours after which it should disperse, either by insolation or the increasing wind flow.

Let us now consider the TAFs and METARs. For simplicity only Edinburgh, Birmingham and Exeter have been used in the analysis for each case. The TAFs were:

EDINBURGH	EGPH 18/10_19Z 09010KT 9999 SCT025=
BIRMINGHAM	EGBB 18/10_19Z 15007KT 9999 SCT026=
EXETER	EGTE 18/07_16Z 11010KT 9999 SCT025 SCT040 TEMPO 0709 4000 SCT004 BKN010=

For those readers who are not fluent in TAF decode language the following offers an explanation of the Exeter forecast. Other readers should jump straight to page 52.

EXETER EGTE	EGTE is the location identifier and is recognised world wide.
18/07_16Z	18 represents the day of the month, 07_16Z shows that the TAF is valid from 0700hrs to 1600hrs Zulu time or UTC, Universal coordinated time.
11010KT	110 means that the wind will be blowing from 110° true, (rounded to the nearest 10°) at 10 knots.
9999	Visibility more than 10km. 0000 would represent a visibility of less than 50 metres.
SCT025 SCT040	SCT is the abbreviation for scattered cloud, 3 to 4 oktas or eighths of coverage. (FEW means 1 to 2 oktas. BKN means broken at 5 to 7 oktas and OVC is the abbreviation for overcast and means unbroken cloud cover.)

	025 and 040 relate to the cloud base in hundreds of feet above the aerodrome level.
TEMPO 0709	This is a trend forecast for the expected weather between the hours of 0700hrs and 0900hrs Zulu.
4000	The expected weather will reduce the visibility to 4,000 metres.
SCT004	The 3 to 4 oktas of cloud will lower to 400 feet above aerodrome level.
BKN010=	There should also be a broken cloud base of between 5 to 7 oktas at 1,000 feet. = means the end of the forecast.

Now, back to the general meaning of the forecasts. The meteorologists expected the Edinburgh wind to be 090° although the form 214 and form 215 show it to be southerly. The average wind over the forecast period is considered and here it should be affected by the centre of the high that will have light, variable winds. Looking back to the form 214 (Figure 10.2) the 55°N 00°E box shows a south easterly surface wind influence and the 55°N 0230W box is southerly.

Birmingham's forecast wind is confirmed by all the other data, close to southerly, parallel to the isobars, with a gentle breeze. Exeter has more of an easterly wind as confirmed by the form 214 and this is due to the clockwise air flow around the lower part of the centre of high pressure.

The METARs told a similar story.

EDINBURGH	EGPH 18/0850 05004KT 9999 SCT045 SCT100 BKN250 12/07 Q1019 NOSIG=
BIRMINGHAM	EGBB 18/0850 14007KT 9999 SCT012 SCT140 BKN220 11/08 Q1021 NOSIG=
EXETER	EGTE 18/0850 12007KT 9000 SCT020 BKN045 14/13 Q1019=

METARs use similar decodes to TAFs. The exceptions are the time group and the inclusion of the dewpoint, ambient temperature and QNH.

The time given is that of the time of observation, in the example above, 0850hrs Zulu or UTC. Information following this time is in the same format as that for a TAF until the temperature is quoted. The 12/07 and 11/08 in the Edinburgh and Birmingham reports show that the temperatures are 12°C and 11°C respectively, whereas the dewpoints are 7°C and 8°C. The closer the dewpoint the more humid the air and, as a result, the worse the visibility. This is confirmed by the visibility for Exeter. It is reported as 9000 metres with a temperature/dewpoint difference of only 1°C.

The QNH for each aerodrome is given at the end of the report and before the trend, if any. QFE can be *approximated* by reducing the QNH by one millibar for each thirty feet the aerodrome lies above sea level.

The trend indicator always follows the actual weather report and is a short term landing forecast valid for two hours forming a mini-forecast under one or more of the following categories:

CAVOK	Good VMC flying weather but with reservations. See page 129 for details.
BECMG	A gradual change at a constant rate. This may be followed by a UTC time group (hours and minutes) preceded by FM (from), TL (until) or AT (at).
INTER	Intermittent changes with conditions fluctuating.
NOSIG	No significant changes expected.
PROB	Percentage of probability of a change occurring.
RAPID	Rapid change occurring in ½ hour or less.
TEMPO	Change expected to last for less than one hour. As with BECMG, this may be followed by a time group and FM, TL or AT.

These abbreviations, where applicable, are followed by a forecast in the same code as the original report or forecast.

All the actual winds were lighter than forecast at 0850 but bear in mind this is early in the day and the TAF covers the period 1000 – 1900hrs. The wind directions were accurate apart from Edinburgh that had a light breeze from 050° which, considering such a low speed of general airflow can easily veer or back locally.

The visibility was good except for Exeter which, being on the coast, would experience a moist air flowing directly off the sea. This is also reflected in the temperature and dewpoint. They are very close at only 1° apart suggesting that mist or fog are likely. The TAF for the period 0700 – 0900 hrs anticipates the visibility to be down to 4000 metres. With such saturated air, the temperature and dewpoint can be assumed to be equal. Cloud in all areas is scattered and would be likely to dissipate further during the day due to surface heating.

Finally the QNH. This shows accurately the left-hand bulge of the high pressure system where the pressure increases to 1021 over Birmingham confirming the high's position as drawn on the charts.

It is possible to read the wind strength directly off the surface analysis charts by using the geostrophic wind scale box. Simply measure the distance between the isobars on the chart over the required area. This can be done accurately, either with a pair of dividers, or by marking the side of a sheet of paper. Always measure parallel to the line of latitude. Check the latitude at which this point lies, these are marked on the chart and as a guide the 50° line is just below the south of the UK. Now compare the measured distance

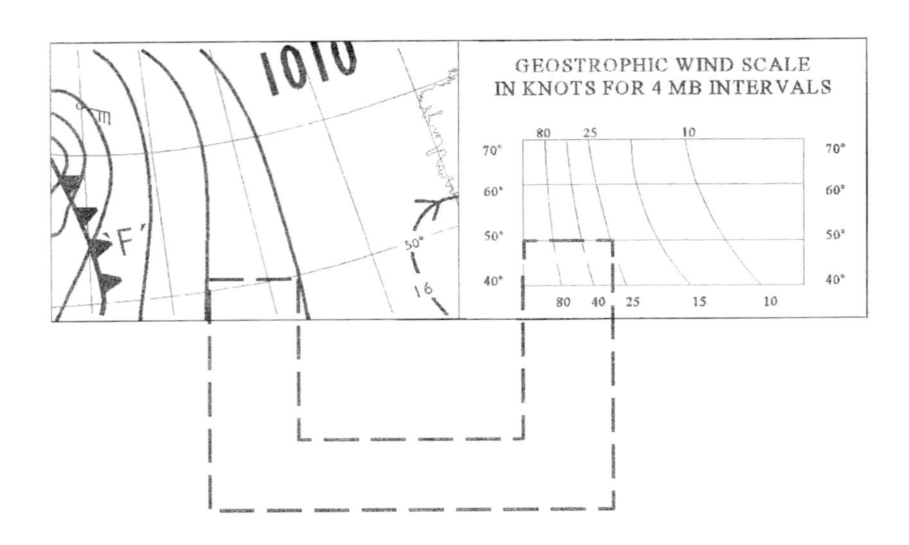

Figure 10.4 The actual windspeed across these isobars is 25 knots. The windspeed can be read directly off the surface analysis charts by measuring the distance between the isobars as parallel as possible to the lines of latitude and comparing the distance to the geostrophic wind scale. Always measure from the left and remember the closer the lines, the stronger the windspeed.

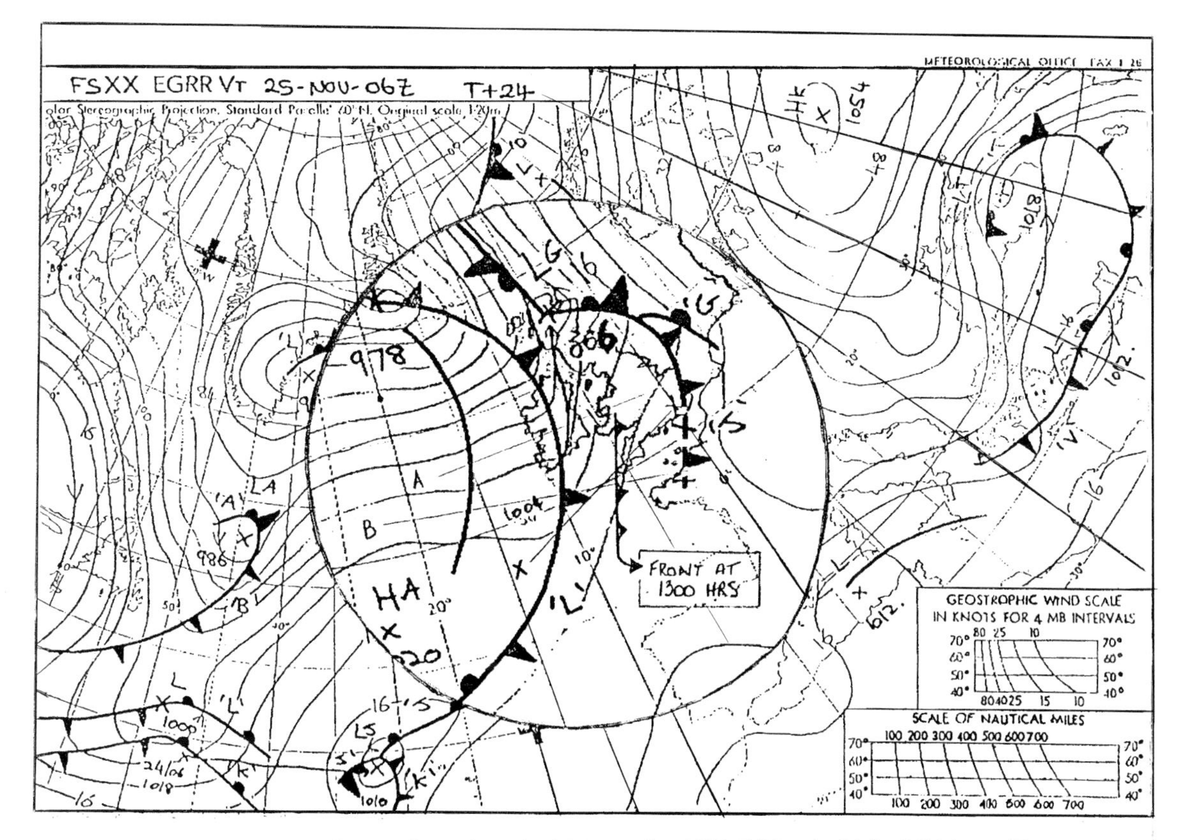

Figure 10.5 Surface analysis chart for 25 November 1993 T(Time)+24 for 0600 hours Z.

with the geostrophic wind scale box for that latitude using the left-hand side of the box as the start for your first mark. Read across to the right and this will give the wind speed. Remember that the closer the isobars the stronger the wind. Taken off the chart (shown on page 55) the wind speed over south-west England will be about 25 knots. At Liverpool and towards the tip of Scotland it will be about 35 knots, reducing towards the northern coast.

More useful than knowing the wind speed at a location is calculating the time a front will pass your airfield or, if you are flight planning a route, what time you will meet a front. Those readers who go on to take the instrument rating will be supplied with 1:5,000,000 charts. These are available from some met offices and can be used to plot frontal movements very accurately. If you cannot get hold of these, surface analysis charts give the required detail and have wind speed and distance scales. From these we can calculate rough frontal passage times and for the private pilot this is as accurate as you need to get.

In the example at Figure 10.5 a cold front lies across Ireland. Let us assume we want to fly from Bournemouth to Land's End with a

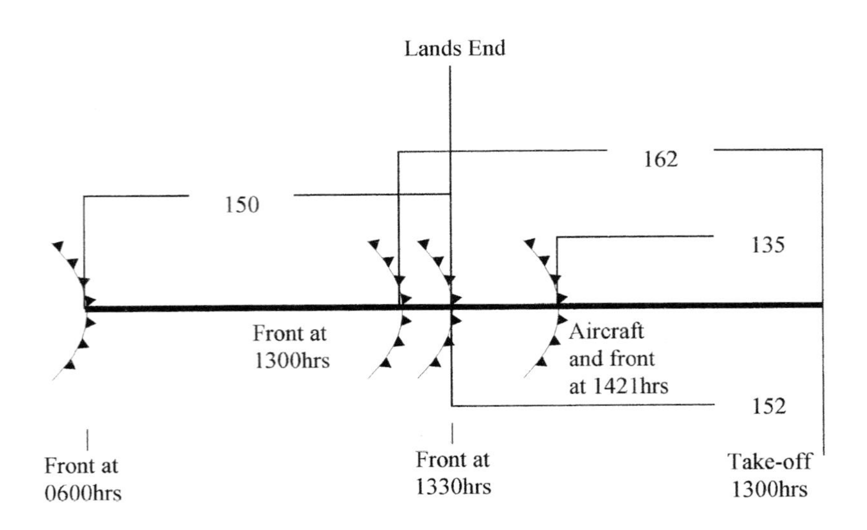

Figure 10.6 Simplified chart showing the calculations for the times and positions of the aircraft and front.

departure time of 1300hrs Zulu and a ground speed of 100 knots. This should take one hour 30 minutes. If you want to follow this process in detail, you could obtain a full size surface analysis chart and copy across the cold front and isobar positions. A simplified version is shown at Figure 10.6.

First we need to know the speed at which the front is moving. This is calculated by drawing a line to plot your track, line X on the chart at Figure 10.5. Then a line perpendicular to the frontal section nearest to your intended track, parallel to the isobars. In this case we have line A and B. Measure the geostrophic wind distance across these isobars and compare this with the geostrophic wind scale. Bear in mind that the scale varies with latitude, here we're using the 50° line.

This figure is the speed at which the front is moving. The distance between the isobars each side of the A line measures 25 knots. Across line B measures about 17 knots. We can assume that the path affecting our track averages at around 20 knots.

First let us calculate the time the front will reach Land's End. The frontal position at 0600 hours is 150 miles off the mainland, again we must measure this using the 50° latitude distance scale. To travel 150 miles at 20 knots will take it 450 minutes so it will reach Land's End at 1330 hours.

Things get a little more complicated if we start moving towards or away from the front. In this example we are moving towards the front so we must calculate the position of the front at our time of departure. As we know it will be at Land's End at 1330. We can take 30 minutes off that time to give the position. 30 minutes at 20 knots will put it 10 miles off Land's End.

To find the closing speed we must add the frontal speed to our ground speed as the two are converging. 20 knots + 100 knots = 120 knots. If the front was moving away, the frontal speed must be taken away from the ground speed.

Now measure the distance between the front and the departure aerodrome at the time of take off. This is 162 miles. At the closing speed of 120 knots the interception will take 81 minutes making it 1421 hours.

Taking it one stage further you can now find the position of the interception by calculating its position after eight hours 21 minutes (0600 hours to 1421hours). At 20 knots for 497 minutes = 165 miles from the 0600 hours position. To double check, calculate that the aircraft's position is the same by calculating the distance based on 100 knots for one hour 21 minutes. This puts the aircraft 135 miles along its track from Bournemouth, 17 miles from Land's End. Using the scale of surface analysis charts you will not get precise times or positions but you should be within 10 miles or 10 minutes at worst. In this example you could have elected to make a VFR flight providing your take off time was 1130hrs or earlier, with the knowledge that the front would pass over while you were happily sitting in the clubhouse at Land's End.

Example Two - Tuesday 12 October

Another day's charts and reports are given at Figures 10.7, 10.8 and 10.9. The surface analysis chart shows a complicated mess of fronts accompanied by a low pressure area affecting the whole of the UK. The low is being fed by arctic maritime air that is journeying well south before being pulled back up. This southern route will modify the temperature causing it to warm and become unstable.

Although air from this source region already has a high humidity, this airflow has had a long journey over the ocean that will result in it becoming very moist and at times, saturated. Within the frontal activity we would expect heavy showers and low cloud. The isobars are well spaced over the south of England that denotes a low wind speed, but closely spaced in southern Scotland where a comparatively high wind speed will be experienced. This area also has a southerly moving occluded front, as does north Wales. As these travel down through the country they will bring increased rain, probably heavy and prolonged at times with the possibility of isolated thunderstorms. Visibility will be reduced by mist or fog in places.

The wind chart at Figure 10.8 confirms our expectations. The wind box for southern Scotland gives 030° at 25 knots for the 1,000 feet wind. The 030° can be seen as running parallel to the isobars on the surface analysis chart. A little lower around Birmingham the wind is variable at five knots, again as expected due to the well-spaced isobars. Exeter does not have a wind box over it so we can make a relatively accurate assessment by taking the 1,000 feet wind from the 5230°N 0230°W and 50°N 0230°W boxes and averaging them. This will result in a wind of around 190° at 12 knots.

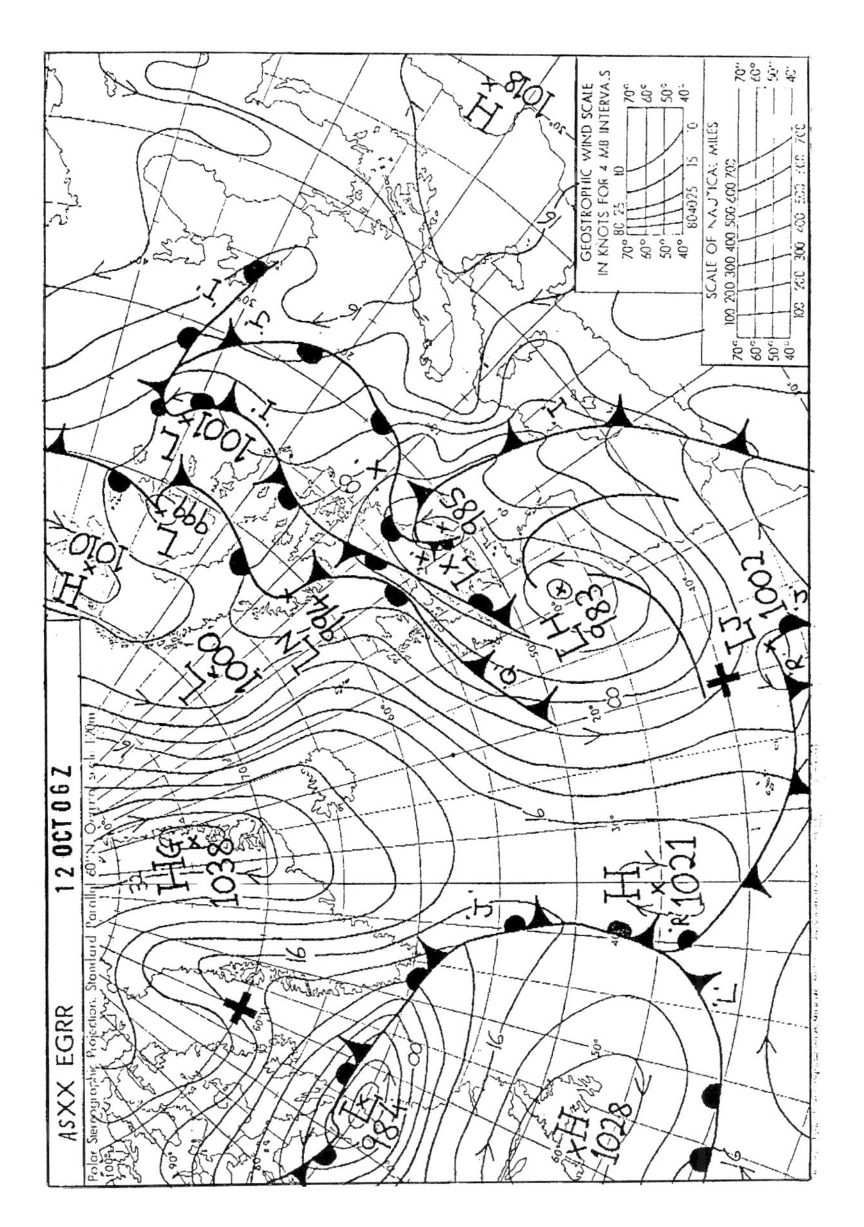

Figure 10.7 Surface analysis chart for 12 October 1993.

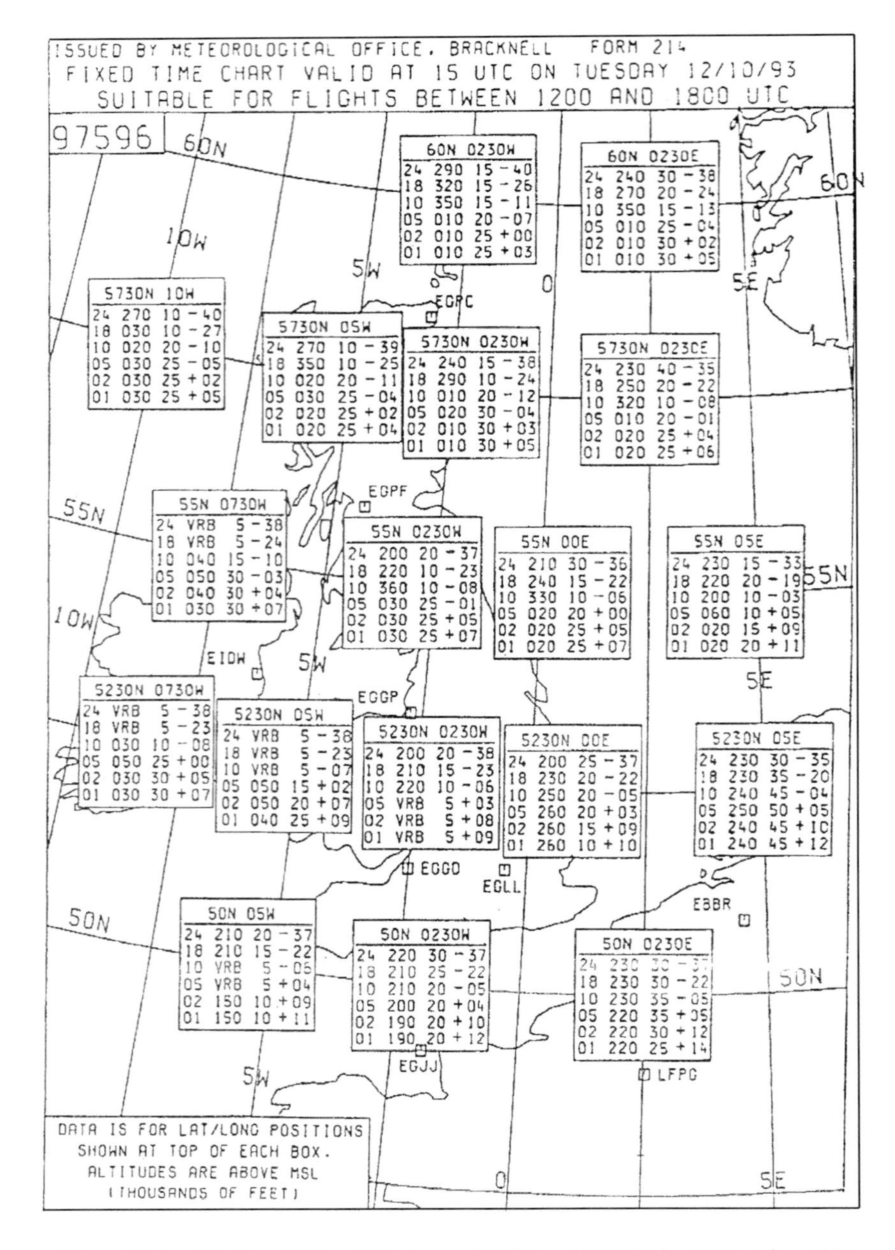

Figure 10.8 Metform 214 valid between 0600Z and 1200Z for 12 October 1993.

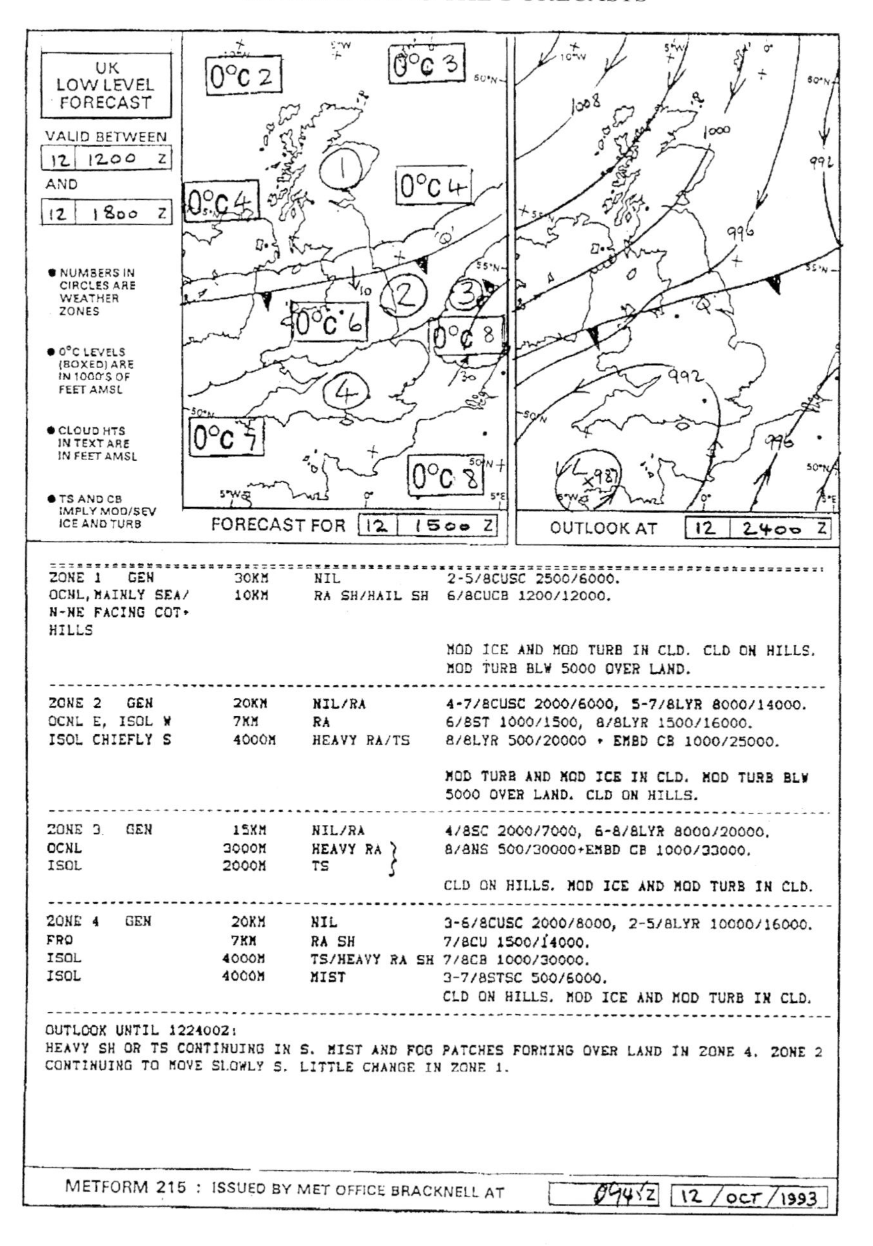

UK LOW LEVEL FORECAST

VALID BETWEEN 12 1200 Z AND 12 1800 Z

- NUMBERS IN CIRCLES ARE WEATHER ZONES
- 0°C LEVELS (BOXED) ARE IN 1000'S OF FEET AMSL
- CLOUD HTS IN TEXT ARE IN FEET AMSL
- TS AND CB IMPLY MOD/SEV ICE AND TURB

FORECAST FOR 12 1500 Z

OUTLOOK AT 12 2400 Z

ZONE 1 GEN	30KM	NIL	2-5/8CUSC 2500/6000.
OCNL, MAINLY SEA/ N-NE FACING COT+ HILLS	10KM	RA SH/HAIL SH	6/8CUCB 1200/12000.
			MOD ICE AND MOD TURB IN CLD. CLD ON HILLS. MOD TURB BLW 5000 OVER LAND.
ZONE 2 GEN	20KM	NIL/RA	4-7/8CUSC 2000/6000, 5-7/8LYR 8000/14000.
OCNL E, ISOL W	7KM	RA	6/8ST 1000/1500, 8/8LYR 1500/16000.
ISOL CHIEFLY S	4000M	HEAVY RA/TS	8/8LYR 500/20000 + EMBD CB 1000/25000.
			MOD TURB AND MOD ICE IN CLD. MOD TURB BLW 5000 OVER LAND. CLD ON HILLS.
ZONE 3 GEN	15KM	NIL/RA	4/8SC 2000/7000, 6-8/8LYR 8000/20000.
OCNL	3000M	HEAVY RA	8/8NS 500/30000+EMBD CB 1000/33000.
ISOL	2000M	TS	
			CLD ON HILLS. MOD ICE AND MOD TURB IN CLD.
ZONE 4 GEN	20KM	NIL	3-6/8CUSC 2000/8000, 2-5/8LYR 10000/16000.
FRQ	7KM	RA SH	7/8CU 1500/14000.
ISOL	4000M	TS/HEAVY RA SH	7/8CB 1000/30000.
ISOL	4000M	MIST	3-7/8STSC 500/6000.
			CLD ON HILLS. MOD ICE AND MOD TURB IN CLD.

OUTLOOK UNTIL 122400Z:
HEAVY SH OR TS CONTINUING IN S. MIST AND FOG PATCHES FORMING OVER LAND IN ZONE 4. ZONE 2 CONTINUING TO MOVE SLOWLY S. LITTLE CHANGE IN ZONE 1.

METFORM 215 : ISSUED BY MET OFFICE BRACKNELL AT 0945Z 12/OCT/1993

Figure 10.9 Metform 215 valid between 0600Z and 1200Z for 12 October 1993.

The Metform 215 at Figure 10.9 splits the country into four zones; for this example we will ignore zone 3 as it does not affect mainland UK. Zone 2 shows that the frontal systems shown on the surface analysis chart will evolve into one southerly very slow moving cold front.

Note that there is hardly any expected frontal movement for the full forecast period as it is shown as moving south at 10 knots. This area will experience the weather associated with the normal passage of a front as covered in earlier text. Visibility would be expected to reduce, in places to 4,000 metres, with an overcast cloud base of 500 feet bringing heavy rain and possible thunderstorms.

Zone 1 shows a temperature drop behind the front. This produces a freezing level of 4,000 feet reducing to 2,000 feet as the direct flow of arctic maritime air passes south. Rain would be expected and hail likely as the air becomes unstable as it travels, forming well-developed cumulus and cumulonimbus. In these clouds there will be strong updrafts and the air temperature will cause any water droplets above 4,000 feet to become supercooled, or, if sufficient ice nuclei exist, to form hailstones. Visibility behind the front will be good as is usual with an arctic maritime airflow.

Zone 4 covers the south of the country. The freezing level is higher, up to 8,000 feet well clear of the frontal weather zone but the visibility and cloud base will be low in places due to the moist airflow from the Atlantic.

The TAFs for our selected aerodromes gave:

EDINBURGH	EGPH 12/13-22Z 04017G28KT 9999 SCT018 PROB30 1318 9000 –SHRA BKN015=
BIRMINGHAM	EGBB 12/13-22Z 02005KT 7000 BKN008 TEMPO 1319 9999 SCT010 BKN 020 BECMG 2022 5000 RA BKN005=
EXETER	EGTE 12/13-22Z 19006KT 9999 SCT007 BKN030 TEMPO 1322 2000 SHRA BKN005 OVC014=

The Edinburgh TAF confirms the effect of the tightly packed isobars giving an airflow from 040° at 17 knots and gusting up to 28 knots. Good visibility is expected but a 30% probability (*70%*

improbability) of a reduction to 9,000 metres with light (denoted by –) rain showers.

Birmingham's weather starts the day with the front to its north. Confirmed by the slack pressure gradient, the wind will be light, visibility moderate with a broken cloud base at 800 feet. At 1300hrs this is expected to dissipate to scattered cloud and the visibility improve to more than 10km. A gradual change is then expected around 2000hrs as the front approaches with lowering visibility. The cloud base will drop to 500 feet and after the times of this TAF, will eventually become overcast with cumulus, cumulonimbus and nimbostratus as the front passes.

Exeter is forecasting a light breeze, this contradicts the winds given on the form 214 so in our interpretation we would expect them to be higher. We will see later how it turns out in the actual. During the whole forecast period temporary changes, TEMPO, are expected. These are forecast to last for less than one hour and will reduce the visibility to 2,000 metres and a broken cloud base of 500 feet will lie under an overcast stratus layer at 1,400 feet bringing rain showers.

The METARs gave:

EDINBURGH	EGPH 12/1320 04018G29KT 020V080 9999 SCT018CB SCT020 10/04 Q0998 NOSIG=
BIRMINGHAM	EGBB 12/1250 03004KT 9000 SCT008 SCT010 BKN035 11/09 Q0992 TEMPO BKN010=
EXETER	EGTE 12/1250 17010KT 9999 SCT009 SCT013 BKN025 15/14 Q0990=

All these reports are in the form previously covered with the exception 020V080 in the Edinburgh report. The V signifies that there was a significant change in wind direction (60° or more) during the 10 minute period preceding the time of observation.

The Edinburgh actual proved the TAF to be very accurate. The limited visibility and showers have yet to show there or at Birmingham. Note the temperature and dewpoint are close, as confirmed by the visibility of 9,000 metres.

At Exeter the wind is 10 knots, this reflects the form 214 wind boxes but not the TAF. The temperature and dewpoint are only 1° apart which, although not reflected in the 9999 visibility suggests there is a strong possibility of a rapid reduction in visibility. Look at the QNH values for each report and compare them with the form 215. The METAR is not really needed to get this figure as you can average the pressures over your required point from the two nearest isobars.

Chapter 11

Definitions and Effects Associated with Air Masses and Fronts.

The Density and Pressure of Air

If an aircraft flies from an area of warm air to an area of cold air the density increases causing the rectified airspeed to increase. As the definition of rectified airspeed is the indicated airspeed corrected for pressure error it is purely a theoretical consideration for light aircraft pilots but can be calculated by the formula:

$$\text{Density} = \frac{\text{Pressure (millibars)}}{\text{Temperature (°Absolute)} \times \text{Gas Constant}}$$

The International Standard Atmosphere states that the density of air at mean sea level is 1225 grammes per cubic metre. This reduces with height dependent on the local temperature. To calculate the reduction apply the formula:

Density height change per millibar =

$$\frac{96 \text{ x Mean Temperature (°Absolute)}}{\text{Pressure (millibars)}}$$

Air pressure changes not only with height but also with temperature. Air expands when warm and will expand upwards and outwards. The height of a mass of warm air will therefore be higher than that of the cold and the datum from which it begins to put pressure on that below it is higher. It is logical then that any vertical point downwards from this datum will record a higher pressure than that of cold air.

To avoid problems pilots should religiously reset the subscale when flying through different altimeter setting regions to ensure adequate terrain clearance. If the flight is non-radio then the regional QNH for the hour and the hour ahead should be obtained. The danger lies in that the instrument will underread if flying from high to low pressure areas and therefore also underread when flying from warm to cold air unless reset.

This can be remembered by *High Low* - *High* and *Low High* - *Low.*

When flying from *High* to *Low* pressure the altimeter shows *High*er than you are. When flying from *Low* to *High* pressure the altimeter shows *Low*er than you are.

Subsidence

Subsidence is a phenomenon frequently occurring in polar highs where there is an extensive area of sinking air. Just as warm air rises, cold air falls, and the subsiding air is warmed adiabatically with the increase in pressure. It becomes stable as it reaches a point where it is not warm enough to rise nor cold enough to fall further. Subsidence accompanies divergence in the lower layers of the atmosphere. (see Figure 11.1)

Convergence

When two opposing streams of air meet they will flow to the area of lowest pressure. As the air streams are pressing upon one point, or convergence line, some release must be found. As pressure reduces with height, an upward flow forms until the pressure equalises. The opposite effect is called **divergence.** (see Figure 11.2)

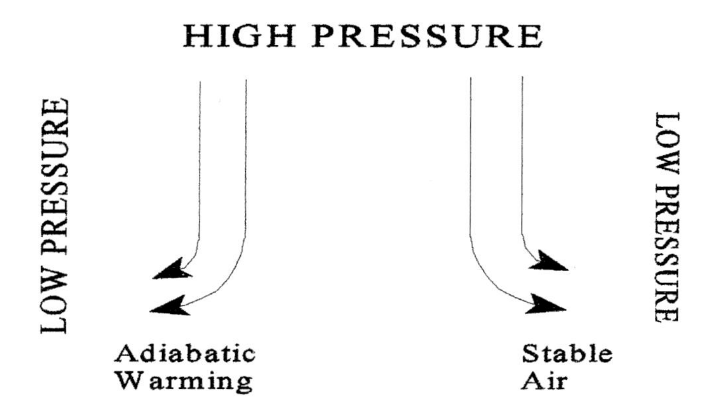

Figure 11.1 A simple illustration of subsidence

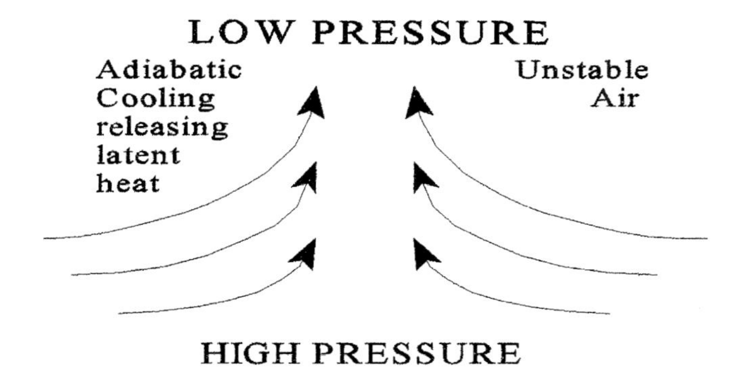

Figure 11.2 A simple illustration of convergence

Frontal Lifting

Frontal lifting is the term used to describe the lifting effect of a mass of warm air being forced to rise over a colder air mass ahead of it or a warm air mass being lifted by cold air behind it.

Quasi-Stationary Front

A front that is almost stationary is called a quasi-stationary front; it can also be called a stationary front, and its position appears almost unchanged on successive synoptic charts. Wave-like disturbances often form in this type of front. The equivalent American expression is to describe such a front as having stalled.

Col

A col is the name given to the situation where an area is surrounded by two diagonally opposed depressions and two diagonally opposed anticyclones. Winds do not circulate around it but flow towards and away from it. No standard weather phenomena results from a col and anything may occur except strong winds at low level.

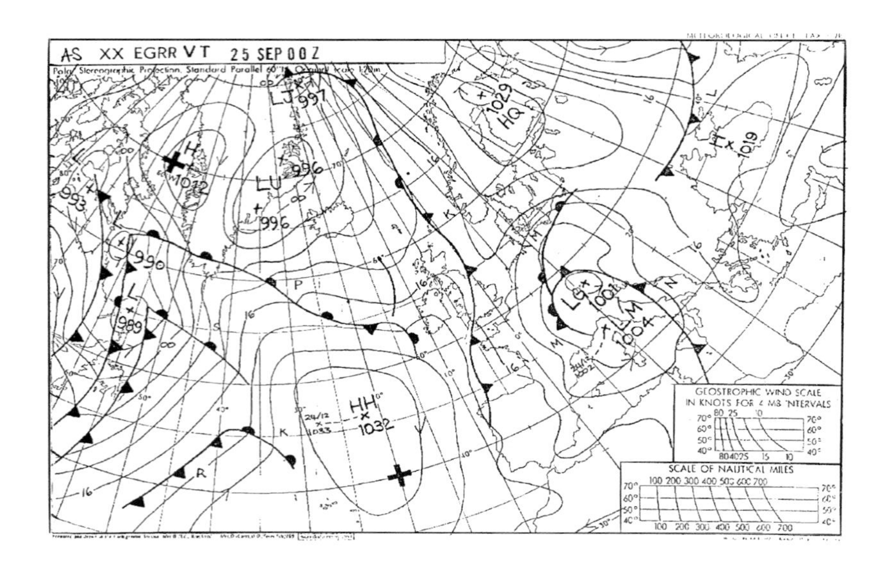

Figure 11.3 A perfect example of a Col. This is an area surrounded by a pair of diagonally opposed high pressure systems and two diagonally opposed low pressure systems. This particular example shows a very slack pressure gradient over the UK. Note the massive trailing intermittently warm and cold front running from the Arctic Circle right down to 40° North latitude.

Chapter 12
Icing

The Bergeron Process or Ice Crystal Theory

Ice Crystal theory, also known as the Bergeron–Findeisen theory, dictates that for precipitation, that is rain, snow or hail, to fall, there must be ice crystals present in the upper part of the cloud. As the cloud develops, the water droplets in the segment above freezing level become supercooled while others will freeze. The proportion of frozen droplets increases with height and the reduction in temperature. The size of the droplets increase by sublimation or by collision with supercooled droplets until they are unable to be supported by the updrafts and start to fall. They increase in size by collision with other droplets during the descent. They will reach the ground either as a solid or a liquid dependent on the temperature.

The theory does not offer an explanation as to how precipitation is formed in clouds where no part of it is above freezing so perhaps Bergeron formed his theory while exclusively experiencing a cold climate.

A Practical (Particle) Theory

Water droplets in a liquid state can exist in a cloud at temperatures as low as -40°C so it is safe to assume that something must trigger them turning into ice. If these droplets hit an aircraft whose skin is below zero they will freeze to form ice. Similarly if they reach frozen ground or vegetation they will turn to ice. So in a cloud they must meet something that allows them to freeze solid.

Analysis of air samples in the atmosphere has shown that it contains a cocktail of particles and bacteria up to a height of 100 kilometres. In the lower levels the presence of salt, ash, unsaturated hydrocarbons and various other flotsam exist; these serve as cloud condensation nuclei. A small percentage of these particles are mineral fragments. Most are blown up from the Earth's surface such as particles of paint, rubber and asphalt from roads and even minerals from volcanic eruptions. A further supply is provided by meteorites burning up on contact with the atmosphere. These particles form ice nuclei and if a supercooled water droplet meets any of these, the droplet will freeze to form hail.

Lots more theories exist, some more unlikely than others, but from the pilot's angle, water does freeze, often with nasty effects.

Carburettor Icing

The common expression carburettor icing is more correctly described as piston engine induction system icing. It can occur in temperatures as high as 30°C increasing in probability proportionately with increasing humidity. The chart that you have no doubt

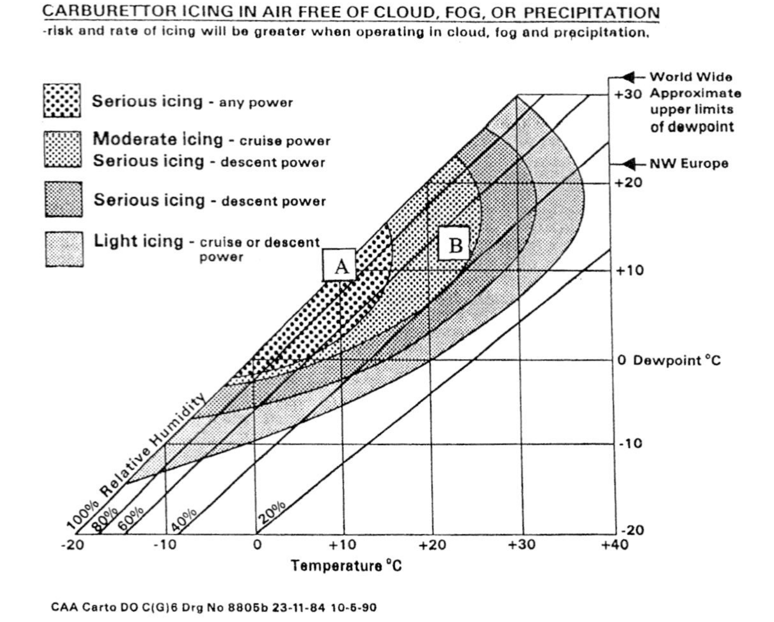

Figure 12.1 The risk of induction system icing increases with temperature and relative humidity.

glanced at before is reproduced at Figure 12.1. Look at it again at the points A & B.

Point A. How often do you happily fly at 3,000 feet in misty conditions? If on that day the ground temperature is a comfortable +15°C the air temperature at that height is +10°C. In misty conditions humidity could be as high as 80%. The proximity of the temperature and dewpoint should alert you to the humidity. You are in prime carburettor icing conditions. Without the regular use of carburettor heat, icing is almost inevitable at any power setting. You should be surprised if you do not get it!

Point B. You are at 9,000 feet, in clear air, 200 feet below a nice level altostratus cloud base. The surface temperature is at +30°C, a heatwave for surface dwellers. If the relative humidity is as low as 50% you risk moderate icing at cruise power and serious icing at descent power. If you are flying close to the base of a cloud the humidity must be high as the moisture is condensing and forming cloud with a temperature change of less than 1°C.

Those are in flight icing conditions. Yet it is possible for these conditions to exist on the ground with icing building up during long taxying or holding times, especially with the engine idling. The first indication will be during power checks when, instead of a slight drop when carburettor heat is applied, an increase in power is noticed. Fortunately this offers a perfect opportunity to clear the ice without worrying about the resultant rough running. Under these circumstances several more carb heat checks should be carried out before you commit yourself to take-off. It is quite possible that the risk of carburettor icing will decrease with altitude but as always, regular, preventive checks must be carried out.

There are three types of induction system icing. Carburettor icing is caused by the sudden drop in temperature due to fuel vaporisation and the reduction in pressure at the carburettor venturi and results in moisture in the induction air forming ice. As a build up increases it restricts the venturi and alters the fuel/air ratio progressively causing a reduction in engine power. Float type carburettors are more prone to this type of icing than pressure jet types. Engines with fuel injection systems are not affected.

Motorcars do not suffer this problem as they are mostly water cooled, resulting in higher temperatures at the air intake. Modern car engines also have a system where the air intake temperature is monitored and increased if required by taking heat from the exhaust

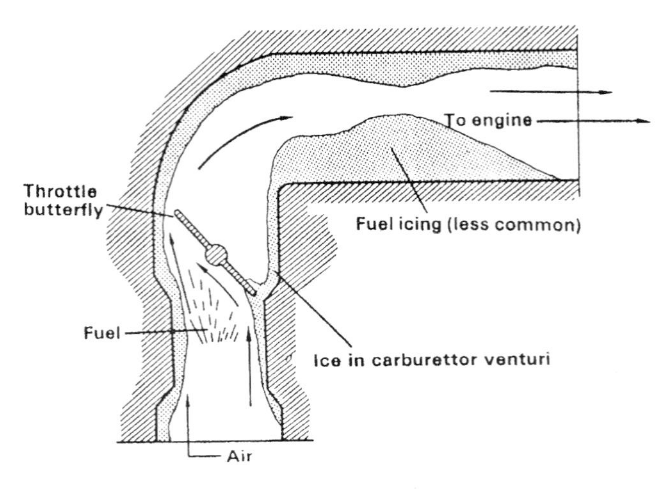

Figure 12.2 The areas affected by a build up of carburettor icing.

manifold. Given that it is fairly dramatic for an aircraft engine to stop in flight, and it is often the probable cause of many incidents, it seems ludicrous that engine designers aren't compelled to include a venturi heating system independent of the exhaust system. A design similar to the pitot head heater would at least offer the chance of a restart.

Reduced power settings, which normally occur in a descent, increase the risk of carburettor icing as the temperature drops at the venturi. Also, the butterfly valve is positioned closer to the casing, reducing the airflow area and increasing the likelihood of an icing restriction.

The stoppage of the fuel flow from the tanks can also be caused by fuel icing. This is where water held in suspension in the fuel can freeze and become a solid. In sufficient quantities it will block induction piping and fuel jets. Because of its greater volatility and possible water content, fuel icing is more likely to occur in Mogas than in Avgas. Water in fuel can come from a contaminated fuel supply or a faulty filler cap but it is much more likely to be from the air itself.

If an aircraft is parked overnight with partially full tanks, the empty part of the tanks will be full of air. As the air above the fuel cools condensation will form on the inner surface of the tank and run down into the fuel. As water is heavier than fuel it sinks and is unable to evaporate or dissipate back into the air. The safest way to avoid fuel icing is to ensure that all tanks are full to the brim before parking up for any period, even overnight.

Impact ice is the general term used for any precipitation that is frozen (sleet or snow) or that freezes on impact with the aircraft, blocking air intakes or filters. It will occur anytime if the temperature of the aircraft is below 0°C but will build up most rapidly at a temperature of -4°C. Fortunately it does not just target intakes and filters so a visual clue will be given by the build up on other parts of the aircraft. If impact ice is encountered or suspected, the alternate air (if fitted) should be selected *ON* immediately in case the selector valve becomes immovable due to packed ice.

Icing Indications

Induction system icing may occur in clear air with the likelihood increasing while in cloud; fuel icing can occur in any conditions if the temperature is below 0°C. The icing chart at Figure 12.1 shows that carburettor icing may occur at temperatures as high as 30°C and the relative humidity as low as 30%. So while flying in the UK and Europe there aren't many occasions when the possibility of carburettor icing should not be anticipated.

Induction system icing is an insidious problem. With a fixed pitch propeller the only indication will be a slight drop in RPM, initially with no other indications or rough running. The pilot's natural tendency to increase the throttle setting will normally mask the problem, so if a couple of slight increases of the throttle setting are required within a short period it should suggest the possibility of icing.

Where a constant speed propeller is fitted the drop in engine power would have to be large before the RPM reduces and the problem could already be serious. The only instruments that will indicate it are the exhaust gas temperature gauge showing a slight drop, and the manifold pressure gauge that will show a clear drop.

Prevention and Cure

Prevention is far better that attempting a cure once the problem is fully established. Dependent on temperature and humidity, the carburettor heat should be applied at regular intervals.

If the engine runs roughly on the application of carburettor heat, under no circumstances must the setting be returned to cold. The rough running will be caused by ice being ingested into the engine and melted. This is reassuring proof that the heat is working, not that something is going wrong.

The heat must be kept fully on (unless otherwise specified in the operating manual) for 15–20 seconds and time allowed between applications for the heat exchanger to reheat. If icing does form a blockage and the engine stops, carb heat probably will not help as the hot air from the heat exchanger cannot be drawn through the carburettor even if the propeller is windmilling. Even if a partial melt is achieved, the hot air supply probably won't be replenished in time for the blockage to be cleared. The moral is simple. Carburettor heat is preventive maintenance, not a last minute cure. Regular use keeps the heart rate down!

Technically the typical requirement of a heat exchanger is that it will provide a temperature rise of 50°C at 75% power, so it follows that the heat exchanger will take some time to reheat after application.

Particular use of carburettor heat should be made in the circuit and approach to land. (Refer to your pilot's operating handbook or manual). Bear in mind that icing risk increases with reduced power such as on final approach. If a go around is required, full power is essential. On most engine types it is recommended that the heat be selected to cold for the last few hundred feet of descent to ensure full power is available.

Airframe Icing

The Theory

Airframe icing will only occur when the ambient and airframe temperatures are both below 0°C. For ice crystals to form water droplets they require ice nuclei. These are not present in the atmosphere in such great quantities as condensation nuclei and so there are often not enough ice nuclei to match the number of droplets. As a result the water droplets continue to be cooled below 0°C and remain in liquid form. The temperature drop can be as low as -40°C and at any temperature below 0°C the droplets are called supercooled water droplets (SCWDs). These SCWDs exist most often between -1°C and -10°C.

If an aircraft, with its skin below 0°C, comes in to contact with SCWDs it will act as the ice nuclei and the droplet will turn to ice attaching itself to the airframe. The extent of icing is controlled by the temperature of the SCWD and its weight. For a liquid to change to a solid the latent heat stored in the droplet must be released.

One gram of water needs approximately 80 calories of latent heat to change from ice to liquid, for the reverse to occur 80 calories of latent heat must be released. One calorie of heat energy is required to raise the temperature of one gram of water by 1°C. It follows that for each degree centigrade that a SCWD is below 0°C, 1 eightieth part of it will freeze on impact. For example if a SCWD is -20°C on impacting the airframe one-quarter will freeze instantly, the rest will freeze as it flows back over the airframe.

Any in flight icing can produce a threat to flight safety. It is important for a pilot to recognise the conditions that will produce icing and avoid them. Some aircraft are cleared for flight in icing conditions; they use de-ice systems that are usually alcohol based as alcohol will only freeze below -117°C.

In Practice

Icing occurs in various forms and is categorised by its appearance. Meteorological warnings of icing only specify light, moderate or severe. They do not specify a type.

Clear ice, which is also known as glaze ice, forms on aircraft that are flying through temperatures of 0°C or lower in rain or cloud. It is often encountered when an aircraft is flying in a cold sector and towards a warm front. The rain falling from the warm front passes through the sub-zero air of the cold front, becoming supercooled (see Figure 12.3). As it contacts the airframe it will form clear ice. Clear ice is difficult to detect and up to two inches of clear ice has remained undetected by crews of large aircraft. It is most likely to form when temperatures are just below freezing and the build up can be very rapid. If a descent is carried out into warmer air, deposits of melting ice can also cause problems by dissipating off the leading edges and either re-freezing elsewhere or, if the build up has been sizable, by departing lumps impacting the tailplane or fin.

Sub-zero temperatures in cloud can result in the formation of rime

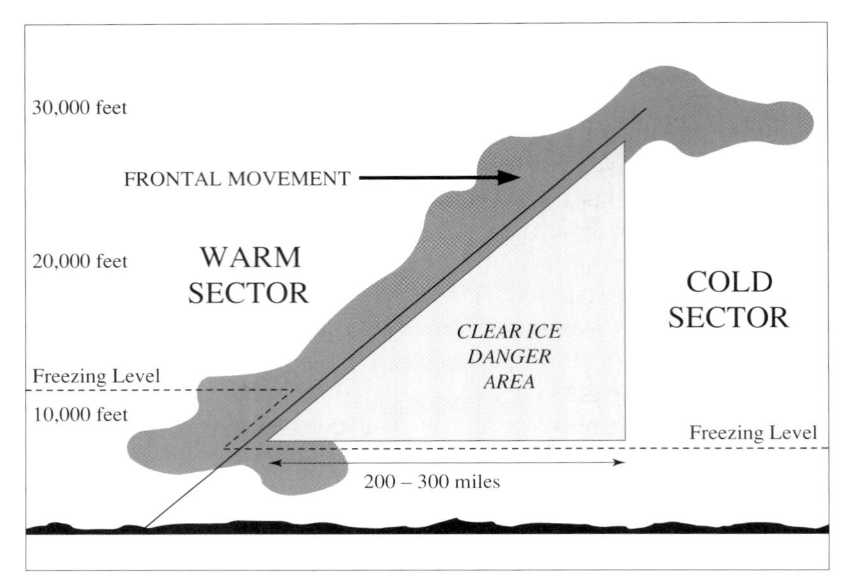

Figure 12.3 A cross-section of a warm front when observed from the surface showing the clear air icing area. This diagram shows the risk area to be around 10,000 feet but this triangle could start from any height. During winter it's possible for the area to be from the surface upwards making the only flight option a 180° turn if icing is encountered.

ice. This is the term used to describe the milky and opaque granular deposit of ice that forms by the rapid freezing of small supercooled water droplets as they strike an airframe. It only occurs in cloud of low water content and is most likely in temperatures well below 0°C. At heights below the 0°C isotherm level (a line joining points of equal temperature) obviously no icing risk exists. At temperatures between -10°C and -40°C a risk of rime ice still exists but this reduces with height as the moisture content of the air diminishes.

In most clouds at -20°C or less, the composition will be mostly ice crystals that simply bounce off the airframe. With more active updrafts in clouds such as cumulonimbus, supercooled water droplets may be carried up to great heights and in such quantities that they are unable to find sufficient icing nuclei. When they fall, still as supercooled droplets, they freeze on impact with an airframe, forming clear ice.

Cloudy or mixed ice is another formation that can quickly coat any aircraft. It forms on an aircraft flying through a cloud containing various sizes of supercooled water droplets, ice crystals and snowflakes. On impact, the combinations form a rough, cloudy deposit.

Hoar frost forms in flight or on the ground. In flight it occurs when an aircraft has been cruising at a height above the freezing level. As the aircraft then descends into an area of warmer air the moisture in the air will attach to the sub-zero airframe by sublimation. This is the name given to the process where water vapour turns directly to ice, or vice versa, without passing through the liquid stage.

This type of icing is the least dangerous as it will disappear quickly when the temperature of the airframe is raised by entry into warmer, above 0°C, air. There can be some temporary effects where cockpit visibility is suddenly lost and VHF radio interference may also be encountered.

Icing on the Ground

Hoar frost occurs on nights when the temperature falls below zero and an aircraft has been left outside. If air is dry it may cool to 0°C without reaching its dewpoint and sublimation will occur when it contacts the skin of the aircraft. It is most likely during anticyclonic conditions with light winds and clear skies. As with all types of frost all traces must be removed before take-off as the performance of the aircraft can be seriously degraded.

Clear ice formed on an aircraft while on the ground is called glazed frost. It occurs when rain falls through a temperature inversion. This is a layer of the atmosphere where the temperature increases with height, such as under an approaching warm front. Rain falls from the front into the sub-zero air below causing it to become supercooled. If the surface, and any aircraft on the ground, are also below 0°C the supercooled droplets will form a thick, heavy sheet of ice on aircraft, taxiways and runways.

Rime frost forms when fog drifts over frozen or snow-covered surfaces during the winter. The air in contact with the surface cools initially to dewpoint temperature to form freezing fog. Further cooling results in the fog becoming supercooled and on impact with any object, forms rime ice. The deposit gives an uneven, white, opaque appearance composed of droplets containing small air pockets. This is the type of frost that covers grass on crisp winter mornings.

Jet and Turbine Icing

For pilots lucky enough to get access to more advanced aircraft with jet or turbine engines, icing can still be a problem. Although cruising levels are usually well above all but a determined cumulonimbus formation, even these aircraft have to descend to light aircraft levels for an approach to land. Besides the types of airframe icing discussed above, these engines also face some additional perils.

Air intakes can be affected by impact icing with supercooled water droplets freezing on to the intake rim, braces and the first stage of the compressor, but the high temperatures inside the engine immediately melt any potential ice formation. Ice guards are provided to protect the intake from large pieces of breakaway impact ice.

Adiabatic cooling at high RPM speeds can result in a drop of up to 5°C and, if the humidity is sufficient, engine icing may occur. Prevention and removal methods include circulating a heated fluid around the intake and induction areas, alcohol-based fluids introduced into the fuel to prevent fuel icing, and hot air from the air intakes blown across the compressor blades.

Chapter 13
Adiabatic Lapse Rates

A term commonly used when studying weather is the adiabatic lapse rate. This is because these rates determine whether an air mass is stable or unstable, and whether cloud will form or dissipate.

The environmental lapse rate (ELR) describes the actual rate at which air temperature changes with height. The International Standard Atmosphere (ISA) environmental lapse rate is quoted as a 1.98°C reduction per 1,000 feet but this, in practice, is rarely the case. The ELR can vary greatly from the ISA to the extent that the temperature may not change with height. It is then referred to as isothermal or as having a zero lapse rate. If the temperature increases with height, a temperature inversion is said to exist.

Adiabatic means *without heat entering or leaving the system* indicating that any temperature changes within a certain volume of air are caused without outside influence. The 'system' is simply a term used to describe a parcel of air. If such an air parcel is forced to descend, the air temperature increases solely due to increased pressure, basically compression, a phenomenon known as adiabatic heating. A simple comparison is a bicycle pump that becomes hot as it is used to compress air. Any air parcel forced to rise, for instance by encountering a mountain, will experience a reduction in pressure permitting it to expand. The temperature of the air consequently drops. A drop in temperature caused solely by the reduction in pressure is known as adiabatic cooling.

To enable us to compare an actual, or environmental, temperature/height lapse rate, two standard rates are used. (See Figure 13.1).

The dry adiabatic lapse rate (DALR) applies to dry unsaturated air. Unsaturated is the term given to an air mass when all the water within it is in vapour form. At the lower levels of the atmosphere dry air cools at the rate of 3°C for each 1,000 feet increase in height.

Saturated adiabatic lapse rates (SALR) apply to saturated air.

This is air that has reached a stage when it can no longer hold water in vapour form. This state occurs when air rises and cools causing condensation to take place. The process induces the release of latent heat that reduces the rate of cooling.

The SALR is consequently 1.5°C for each 1,000 feet but does not remain constant with height. This is because temperature, pressure and the amount of water vapour decreases with height and accordingly the latent heat release reduces. At height, usually above 5,000 feet, the SALR will approach that of the DALR.

Another term that is sometimes used is the superadiabatic lapse rate. Despite its name it is simply a general phrase used to describe any lapse rate greater than the dry adiabatic lapse rate.

For rough, non-exam, calculations, a rough guide to the average temperature lapse rate is 2°C for each 1,000 feet up to 5,000 feet, and 3°C above that. Using this rate you can quickly calculate if a flight in cloud will put you below the freezing level.

The simple fact that warm air rises explains the reason for differing states of instability or stability. These states are given various definitions.

Absolute Stability exists when the ELR is less than the dry and saturated adiabatic lapse rates. Simply put, the lifted air results in very little turbulent activity. The graph at Figure 13.2 shows an ELR of 1°C/1,000 feet that will have a temperature of 5°C at 5,000 feet. If a parcel of dry air enters this environment and is forced to rise it will reduce in temperature to -5°C at this height. It will then be colder than the mass surrounding it and will descend towards its original height. If saturated air is forced to rise within a similar mass it will cool to 2.5°C at 5,000 feet, again cooler than the mass surrounding it. Its ascent will stop and it will then descend.

In the example below, and all the other graphs in this section, a surface temperature of 10°C has been used. This could be any value and an actual ELR could have any lapse rate, the SALR and DALR however, will remain constant.

Absolute Instability occurs when the ELR is greater than the dry and saturated adiabatic lapse rates. This results in the parcel of air that is cooling at a greater rate descending, while the warmer, dry and saturated air, will ascend. In the example below the ELR is 4°C/1,000 feet. Dry or saturated air forced to rise within this environment will remain warmer at all heights and continue to rise causing instability.

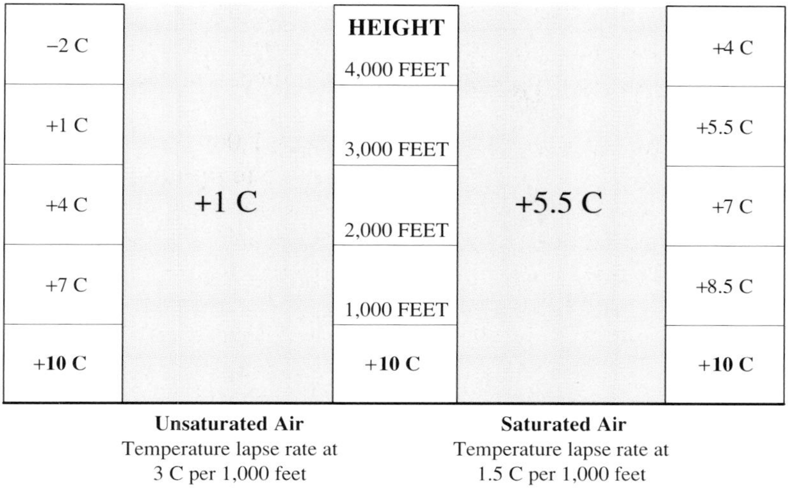

	Unsaturated Air	HEIGHT	Saturated Air	
−2 C		4,000 FEET		+4 C
+1 C		3,000 FEET		+5.5 C
+4 C	+1 C	2,000 FEET	+5.5 C	+7 C
+7 C		1,000 FEET		+8.5 C
+10 C		**+10 C**		**+10 C**

Unsaturated Air
Temperature lapse rate at
3 C per 1,000 feet

Saturated Air
Temperature lapse rate at
1.5 C per 1,000 feet

Figure 13.1 The temperature reductions with height affecting saturated and unsaturated air masses. In this example if the surface starting point temperatures were both 10°C the saturated air would be 5.5°C after it had risen 3,000 feet and the unsaturated air 1°C.

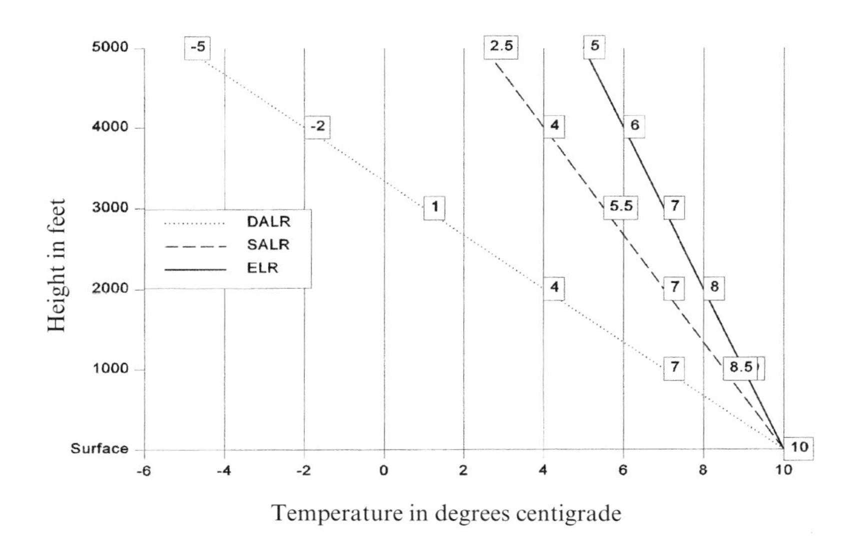

Figure 13.2 The conditions required for absolute stability.

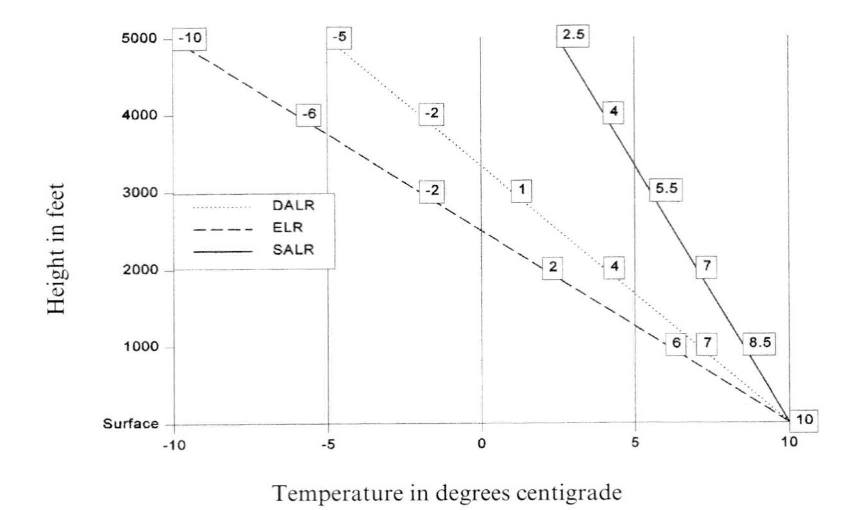

Figure 13.3 The conditions required for absolute instability.

From the illustration at Figure 13.3 we can see that if saturated air is lifted its temperature at 4,000 feet will be 6° lower than its surface temperature. If the ELR is greater than the SALR the lifted air will be warmer and continue to rise. The dry air's temperature would be -2°C at 4,000 feet, again warmer than the environment's -6°C and continue to rise.

The whole basis of understanding adiabatic lapse rates, stability and instability lies with whether, at various heights, the lifted air becomes warmer or colder than the air surrounding it.

Conditional Instability is the consequence of an ELR being between the dry and saturated adiabatic lapse rates. Unsaturated air will remain stable if it is lifted and saturated air will remain warmer than the environment and be unstable. (see Figure 13.4).

Finally, *Neutral Stability* describes the state when the ELR is equal to the lapse rate of a parcel of air that is being lifted within it. At all heights it is the same temperature as the surrounding air and has no impetus to rise or descend.

ADIABATIC LAPSE RATES

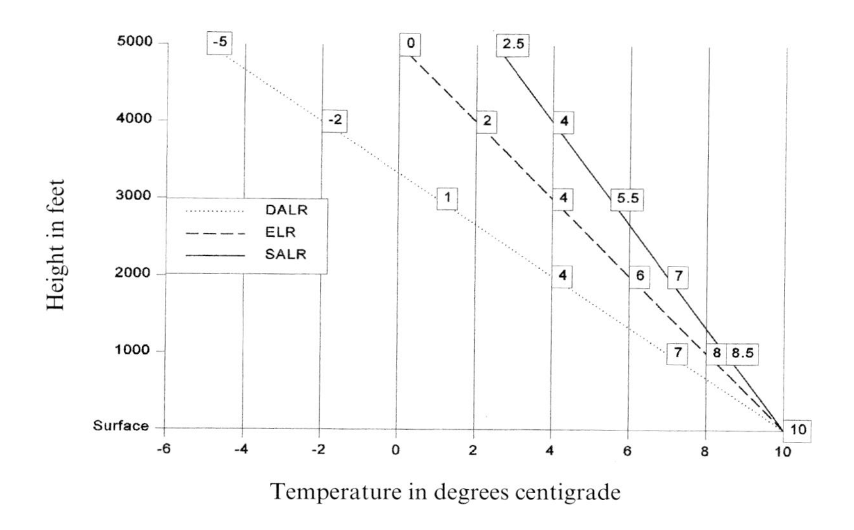

Figure 13.4 The conditions required for conditional stability.

The Latent Heat of Vaporization, Sublimation, Condensation and Fusion

Evaporation is the term given to the process where liquid changes into a gaseous state and is absorbed into the air as water vapour. The process requires the water droplet to release heat and this is termed the latent heat of evaporation or vaporization. It is possible for ice crystals to be vaporized without melting, or for ice to be deposited directly from water vapour. This is known as sublimation.

The Earth's atmosphere is not heated directly by the Sun. The Sun heats the Earth, or objects upon it, and this heat is reflected back into the atmosphere. This is called conduction. Approximately 70% of the Sun's heat that penetrates the Earth's atmosphere reaches the surface. Close to 50% of this heat is reflected back, the remainder increases the surface temperature. Solar radiation in meteorological terms is called insolation.

The temperature of the atmosphere decreases with height as the air gets further away from its heat source. Atmospheric heat dissipates at night when the Sun falls below the horizon and the rays are unable to heat the surface. This rise and fall of the temperature over a 24 hour period is called the diurnal variation of temperature.

The amount of insolation varies with latitude concentrating most strongly on the equator. Maximum daytime temperatures are reached at approximately 1400 hours local time but various factors affect the retained local temperature.

Clouds absorb solar radiation and reflect it back before it can reach the surface but also prevent heat from being radiated back into the atmosphere. In areas where there is a large amount of cloud cover the diurnal variation will be small. Clear, cloud free nights during the winter provide an ideal environment for ground frost as any surface warmth is lost overnight.

The relative humidity of an air mass will also have an eventual effect on its temperature as heat is absorbed from the surrounding atmosphere as water is converted to water vapour. The Sun's rays also heat different surfaces at dissimilar rates. Large areas of water, particularly the sea, change very little over a 24 hour period; usually no more than 1 degree. The Earth's surface is heated more quickly but still reflects much of the heat as do areas of snow or ice that have reflection rates as high as 80%. Areas of vegetation, being mainly water, vary little but built up areas will experience significant temperature changes.

The ratio of the amount of radiant heat reflected back by a surface is known as its albedo and the amount of albedo is expressed as a percentage. The albedo of the Earth–atmosphere system as a whole is estimated to be around 40%.

Heat released or absorbed during changes of pressure is called latent heat. To qualify the description for each set of circumstances a further classification is added.

The *latent heat of evaporation* is the energy required for an air mass to absorb water vapour from a moist source. This energy enables the mass to convert water to water vapour. The heat is stored in the vapour until a further change takes place. The process is also called the *latent heat of vaporization.*

An opposite effect releases the *latent heat of condensation*, but has an apparent side effect. When saturated air is cooled to a temperature below its dewpoint, condensation will occur. As this occurs the latent heat stored in the vapour is released into the atmosphere slowing the rate of cooling. Hence the difference between saturated and dry adiabatic lapse rates. The heat released during the change from water to ice or absorbed in the change from ice to water is called the *latent heat of fusion*.

The final category is the *latent heat of sublimation*. This is the heat released during the change from water vapour to ice or released in the change from ice to water vapour. The subtle difference between this and fusion is that with sublimation there is no liquid stage. Sublimation occurs in practical situations within icing conditions when water vapour may change directly to ice crystals when contacting an aircraft and produce hoar frost.

Actual textbook lapse rate conditions do not often exist and the most common variation is a temperature inversion. This is where the temperature increases with height, as opposed to the normal situation when it reduces. It often marks the height at which a relatively stable cloud formation will level out. Alternatively the temperature may remain constant throughout several thousand feet, in which case the layer is known as isothermal.

At certain aerodromes a warning of a marked temperature inversion is issued when a difference of 10°C or more exists between the surface and any point up to 1,000 feet above the aerodrome. This information is passed to the pilot by ATC and VOLMET broadcasts.

Chapter 14

Clouds, Fog and Precipitation

The definition of a cloud is a mass of air in which condensation has occurred. Water vapour is present in all air masses and is visible in varying degrees dependent on its saturation. Fog and mist are, in a manner of speaking, just thin clouds. This is further confused by low cloud that passes over hills and consequently across the ground. Then the cloud is called hill fog.

The clarification lies in the obsession that, for anything remotely connected with aviation, or meteorology, exact definitions exist.

To become visible, condensation must take the form of very small water droplets of 0.2mm or less in diameter, or for cirrus clouds, ice crystals of the same size. If the base of the cloud is at the surface and visibility is reduced to less than 1,000 metres it is called fog, but where visibility is between 1,000 and 3,000 metres it is known as mist.

For cloud to form there must be a supply of moist air, usually originating from maritime regions, together with some form of cooling process. This is normally adiabatic and due to the air mass being lifted. There can be various causes of this uplift but aside from frontal lifting it is mainly due to turbulence or orographic lifting. Turbulent cloud usually results in layer or stratiform cloud formations that bring light showers or drizzle. This is because there are insufficient updrafts within the depth of the cloud to cause prolonged collisions which would result in the formation of large droplets. As the amount of lift is limited to the level cloud ceiling, flight above the cloud will be smooth. In cloud there will be light to moderate turbulence, forward visibility will naturally be nil and visibility below the cloud base will usually be poor.

Orographic lifting is the term given to the disturbing effect of hills or mountains on an air mass flowing horizontally across the Earth's surface. It can result in various cloud types dependent on whether the lifted air is stable or unstable. Stable air will form stratiform clouds with similar characteristics to turbulence clouds. Unstable air will form cumuliform clouds, with their development being bound by the extent of the instability.

Convective lifting can also trigger the formation of cumulus clouds. The process starts at daybreak when, after a clear night, heat radiation from the surface has been strong enough to form an inversion close to the ground. An inversion is a layer of the atmosphere where the temperature increases with height.

By early morning the inversion will have disappeared and the warm surface air mixes with the higher levels. Approaching midday the rising air cools until it reaches saturation level forming the cloud. This will continue until the afternoon when the process will slowly reverse.

Theories on the Creation of Rain

Several theories relate to the reason for rain. The most accepted being the *Coalescence Theory*. This theorises that water droplets become big enough to fall to the surface by collision with other droplets in updrafts. As altitude increases so does the concentration of droplets lifted by updrafts. As they increase in size, the speed at which they are uplifted decreases which increases the probability of collision with smaller droplets from below. When the droplets reach a size that can no longer be supported by the updrafts they fall as precipitation.

The *Particle Theory* contends that the atmosphere contains minute particles of salt, ash and smoke from forest, industrial or domestic fires plus unsaturated hydrocarbons produced by natural vegetation. These particles are effectively cloud condensation nuclei and, when sufficient humidity exists cause water vapour to concentrate into mist or cloud water droplets around them. These droplets increase in size by collision within the normal air circulation of a cloud and when they become too large to be supported by the updrafts, fall as rain.

Water Vapour

Water vapour is the term used to describe particles of water suspended in the atmosphere. The concentration of water vapour in an air mass is dependent on the temperature of the mass. Higher air temperatures can hold a higher proportion of vapour than cold before condensation occurs.

Water vapour is introduced into an air mass by evaporation and while it remains in vapour form the air is said to be unsaturated. If the air cannot absorb any more evaporated water vapour or is cooled so that it can no longer retain the vapour, the air is said to be saturated. It is at that point that condensation takes place. Condensation on this scale results in cloud formations that in turn can lead to precipitation.

The Dewpoint

The only time a dewpoint is likely to be quoted to a pilot is on a METAR, but understanding its significance is useful. By definition the dewpoint is the temperature to which air can cool, with no change of pressure, without condensation occurring. At this temperature the air is saturated and any cooling below this temperature will cause condensation.

Relative humidity and dewpoint can be calculated by the indirect use of wet and dry bulb thermometers. This involves two identical thermometers mounted side by side. One has its bulb covered in a wick that is kept moist by being dipped in water. Evaporation of the water from the wick extracts heat from the bulb and its reading is always lower than that of the dry bulb.

The amount of moisture in the air is proportional to the rate of evaporation of the wick. The drier the air, the greater the rate of evaporation. If the air is saturated, the evaporation will be zero and both thermometers will read the same. Dewpoint and relative humidity can be calculated from tables but the dewpoint is approximately as far below the wet bulb temperature as the wet bulb temperature is below the dry bulb temperature. METARs quote temperature and dewpoint and the closer these are, the higher the likelihood of cloud, mist or fog.

Visibility

Surface or ground visibility during daylight is the distance at which objects of known distance are visible over at least half the horizon. Visibility at night is calculated by how far you would expect to see in the prevailing conditions if it were daylight. Visibility is reported in kilometres or metres and can be reduced by various phenomena. As always, these phenomena are classified into various categories.

Snow is the general term for ice crystals that fall as precipitation, affecting visibility in proportion to their size and intensity. Blowing snow is composed of ice crystals picked up from the ground by a strong surface wind, to a height of at least 6 feet, usually reducing visibility to below 1,000 metres.

When water, whether in liquid or solid form, is introduced into the atmosphere by the wind it is known as a hydrometeor. These can take any form, such as sea spray or blowing snow, and are too variable to be categorised.

Rain is simply water droplets falling as precipitation and affects visibility in proportion to the size of the droplets and their intensity. Drizzle is formed by very small, numerous droplets of water falling as precipitation, reducing the visibility to between 500 and 3,000 metres.

Fog is classed as minute water droplets held in suspension in the atmosphere. These must have a diameter of less than 0.2mm and reduce visibility to less than 1,000 metres. Mist has the same classification as fog except that the visibility is 1,000 metres to 3,000 metres.

Dust or haze is the classification given to minute solid particles held in suspension in the atmosphere reducing visibility to between 1,000 metres and 10 kilometres. Dust storms are almost unknown in the UK and are indigenous to arid areas. They are caused by strong winds and thermal activity which lift dust from arid areas reducing visibility to less than 1,000 metres.

Sandstorms are also very rare in the UK and are confined to localised coastal effects. The effect qualifies as a sandstorm when visibility is reduced to less than 1,000 metres.

Smoke is reported when solid particles introduced into the atmosphere from combustion reduce visibility to less than 1,000 metres.

In Flight Visibility is the average forward horizontal distance, taken from the cockpit of an aircraft, at which prominent unlit objects may be seen and identified by day. At night the same applies to lit objects. The distances are a matter of personal interpretation as there is no reliable method of measurement.

Mist, haze, smoke, diamond dust (ice crystals), dust and sand are not reported unless they reduce visibility to less than 5,000 metres.

Cloud Classifications

Clouds are classified according to their appearance and height above the ground. The following classifications relate to temperate latitudes:

Low cloud	– any cloud type with a base below 6,500 feet.
Middle cloud	– prefixed alto, has a base of between 6,500 and 23,000 feet.
High cloud	– prefixed cirro, has a base between 16,500 and 45,000 feet.
Heap cloud	– forming at any height.

In forecasts (TAFs) and actual reports (METARs) various abbreviations are used. They are based on eighths (1/8ths) of cloud cover. These eighths are called oktas.

SKC	– Sky clear
NSC	– No significant cloud
CAVOK	– Refer to the section on CAVOK (page 129)
FEW	– Indicates 1 to 2 oktas
SCT	– Scattered, indicating 3 to 4 oktas
BKN	– Broken, indicating 5 to 7 oktas
OVC	– Overcast, indicating 8 oktas

Heights in these forecast or actual reports indicate the cloud base and are quoted in hundreds of feet above the aerodrome or ground observation level.

Fog and Cloud Types

Cloud is formed when an air mass cools and becomes saturated. As covered earlier, this can be caused by a large mass movement into a colder area or by more localised effects.

Heat from the Sun warms areas of the Earth's surface at different rates. If the difference covers a large area, convective heating will result. For instance, a city area of concrete and tarmac will heat faster than the area of vegetation around it. The city air will become warmer causing it to become less dense and consequently rise. This type of heating is known as convection. As air rises it cools by expansion and the relative density increases. This situation is true for low to medium level pressure areas but pressure predominantly decreases with height. Relative humidity is the ratio between the actual amount of water present in a parcel of air in comparison to the amount of water that parcel could hold at that temperature and is expressed as a percentage. When an air mass reaches the stage when it cannot hold water in vapour form it is said to be saturated or at saturation point.

The saturation point relates to a relative humidity of 100%. Anything above this level is classed as the dewpoint at which cloud, dew, fog or mist forms. Relative humidity is directly affected by the temperature, the higher the air temperature the more water vapour it will hold before reaching saturation. Relative humidity and dewpoint can be measured with a wet and dry bulb thermometer.

The movement of air masses can be forecast and the way in which they will be modified in relation to temperature and humidity can be predicted. This enables the forecaster to theorise that certain types of cloud and precipitation may occur. The main types are categorised as follows:

Fog

Advection Fog – over land

Advection fog forms over land when a mass of warm air moves over a colder surface causing the air's temperature to drop increasing its relative humidity. If the air is cooled below its dewpoint temperature and a light wind is present (3 – 8 knots), advection fog will form. It can occur during the day or night, whatever the cloud cover, as it is purely a result of the temperature differences between the air and the surface.

The likelihood of advection fog increases if the surface moisture level is high. Most formations at UK latitudes occur between October and March during a slack pressure gradient. They disperse with an increase in wind speed, a change in air mass, or by surface heating.

Advection Fog – over the sea

Advection fog over the sea is formed when tropical maritime (warm, moist) air flows towards the UK. As it passes over the colder sea, it cools, eventually reaching its dewpoint, where condensation occurs as fog. It may occur during the day or night whatever the cloud cover and may penetrate up to 10 – 15 miles inland, although this will usually clear by surface heating. Sea fog forms mainly in winter or spring when the sea temperature is at its lowest. This type of fog will disperse only by a change of air mass and can persist even with a moderate or strong wind.

Frontal Fog

Frontal fog is the name given to cloud which forms close to a weather front along the surface. The area covered by the fog may be as large as the rain belt and as much as 200 miles ahead of the front's surface position. The fog clears with the passage of the front.

Radiation Mist and Fog

Radiation fog forms over low lying, moist, inland areas and is caused by the radiation of heat from the surface into the atmosphere. As the surface temperature drops, usually late afternoon, the air closest to the surface is cooled to its dewpoint temperature causing condensation to form. If the wind is within 3 to 8 knots, the droplets will be held in suspension forming a mist or fog. If the wind is calm only dew results. The fog usually persists overnight until sunrise when the surface is warmed by the Sun. If the fog is sufficiently thick, it prevents the Sun's rays from reaching the surface allowing the fog to remain until a stronger wind or a change of air mass occurs.

Where conditions exist for the likely formation of radiation fog, it is always a good idea to plan for an alternate aerodrome that is situated well above sea level. Six to 800 feet is usually adequate to ensure that if the low lying areas are filled with fog a clear oasis exists above. A valley may fill with fog due to katabatic drainage from the surrounding areas, usually reaching its maximum thickness about one hour after sunrise. As surface heating increases, anabatic winds may form blowing the fog over higher ground. Alternatively, if the prevailing wind increases sufficiently the fog will be blown or dragged out of the valley and over the high ground. (See Figure 14.1).

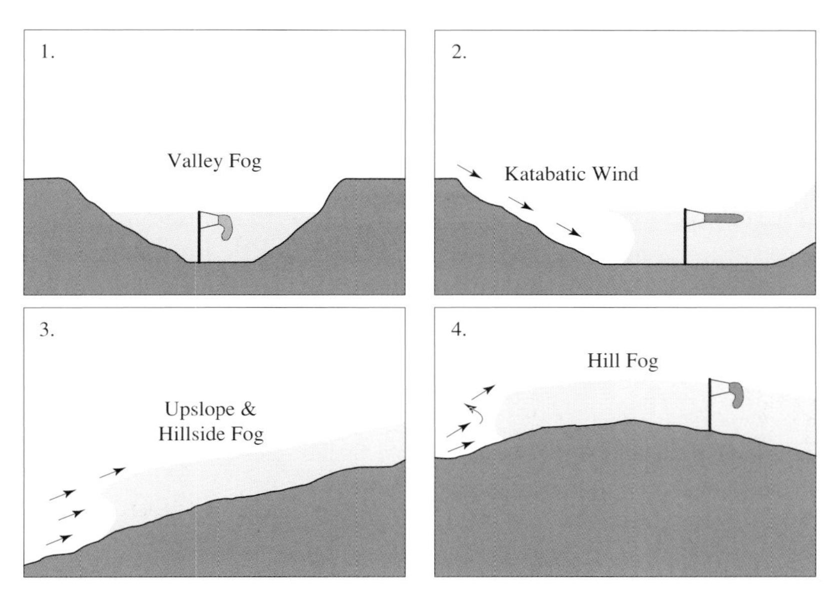

Figure 14.1 A typical valley fog formed by cold air flowing down the hillside and covering a low lying airfield. This is then cleared by an anabatic wind. The fog is pushed up the side of the slope and over the hilltop, covering the airfield on high ground. The fog may remain until surface heating develops or a less localised wind system passes through.

Hill Fog

Hill fog is the name given to two separate phenomena. The type of air associated with cumulus clouds will ensure that as it approaches high ground it will lift and pass over. However, low stratus clouds are contained within stable air that will drift over high ground resulting in the base being on the surface. This is then known as hill fog and may persist until the layer of stratus passes or dissipates.

Hill fog in the more literal sense is caused by orographic lifting of a valley fog up a hillside. It may occur any time of the year and will disperse as the cloud formation is blown away or the base lifts by surface insolation.

In Flight Visibility

All these foggy, misty or hazy conditions become very important when you want to find your destination airfield for a visual approach and landing.

The visibility from the aircraft to the surface is called slant or oblique visibility unless the view is vertical, then it is known as vertical visibility. During anticyclonic periods stable air may cause a haze, mist or fog layer to be trapped near the ground. This layer can be many hundreds of feet thick. Under these conditions ground objects seen from overhead will be hidden from a slant distance. This can be particularly problematical for visual flights.

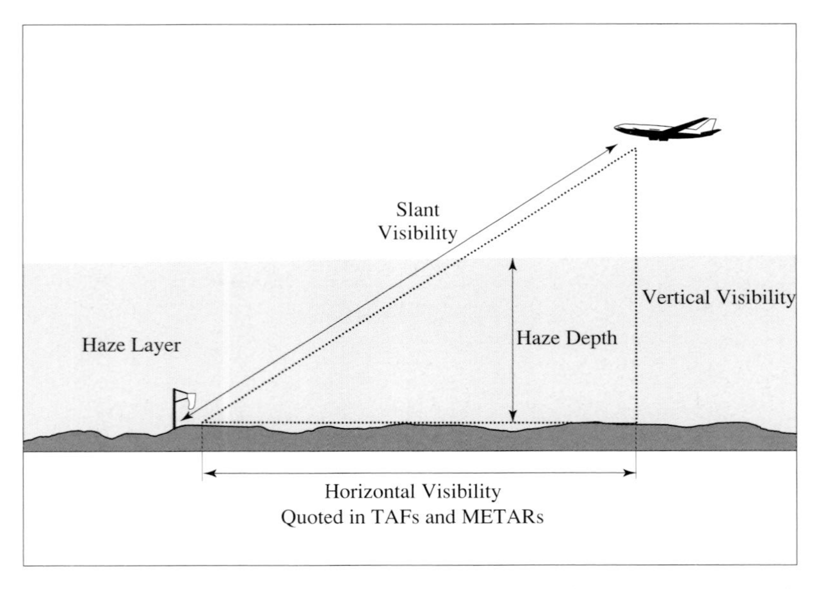

Figure 14.2 The increased depth of haze observed when an object is viewed from a slant.

If, for instance, the layer is 1,000 feet thick when flying over an airfield, you would be looking down through 1,000 feet of haze. If however you were cruising at 2,000 feet looking for the airfield from a distance of 5 miles, you would be looking through a haze layer of more than 30,000 feet.

At lesser distances flying into the sun in haze conditions can result in forward visibility being effectively zero but flying in the same conditions with the sun behind could give a visibility of several miles. In these conditions when approaching an airfield into sun it is worth planning a fix right, left or even past the field to allow for your descent and circuit join with the sun behind you.

Cloud

It is worth learning to recognise and classify cloud types. From their appearance it is possible to gauge whether the air below or within them will be stable or turbulent and whether they should be avoided at all costs. The formation can be predicted by considering the type of air mass and its direction of travel. As discussed before, the cardinal rule for cloud to form is that the air mass must cool. This can be by lifting, contact with a colder air mass, or by passing over a colder surface.

Clouds created in mountainous areas

Banner clouds form when air is forced to rise over a range of mountains. Some of the air finds it easier to go around the peak than over the top and is lifted upwards in back eddies and may form 'windsock' shaped clouds that disperse gradually as the air flows downwind. These clouds are also referred to as cloud banners.

Lenticular clouds often form in mountain waves but can also be found on the leeward side of a large range of hills. The clouds may show as a dotted line decreasing in size downwind or a pile of lens shaped clouds piled upwards showing various saturated levels with clear air between.

Rotor or roll clouds form in areas of mountain wave activity where turbulent up and down drafts swirl around. The clouds are usually cumulus and are accompanied by severe turbulence. Figure 14.3 shows the formation areas of these types of cloud.

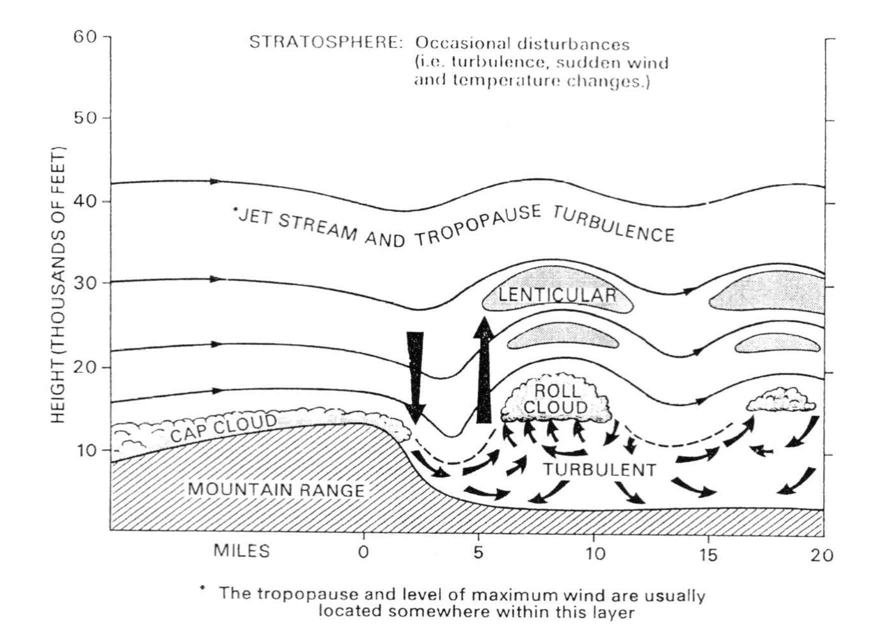

Figure 14.3 The typical features of a mountain wave

A cap cloud will form over the summit of a mountain on a dry day when the air fails to reach its dewpoint at a lower level. The cloud takes the shape of a giant cap perched just off the top of the summit and seems stationary, even with a fresh wind blowing. This is because it is not an individual cloud forming and dispersing as the air sinks and warms on the leeward side but a constantly renewed cloud. As the cloud dissipates it is constantly replaced by new air becoming saturated as it passes over the peak.

Commonplace cloud formations

Cirrus clouds. This is the name given to the highest level of cloud type, usually with a base of 20,000 feet or more. The cloud at this height is composed entirely of ice crystals. The concentration of cirrus may vary. A distant wispy fibrous cloud, often showing the approach of a warm front, may give way to a patchy or rippled effect as in cirrocumulus.

If the sky becomes thinly overcast or veiled by cirrus, it is called cirrostratus. A pattern of cirrus clouds is often called mares' tails.

Cirrus clouds do not cause precipitation, exist in turbulent areas, or present any icing risk. A slowly increasing build up of cirrus is an early indication of an approaching warm front and may be seen hundreds of miles ahead of the front.

More general cloud formations that appear over the UK are cumuliform or stratus clouds. Cumuliform or cumulus have domed shaped upper surfaces and a greater vertical extent in contrast to horizontally extended stratiform types. When the lower atmosphere is well mixed and fairly dry the cloud base may be 4,000 to 6,000 feet above the surface with a very flat level starting point. With stratocumulus formations it may be as low as 1,500 feet.

Strong developments such as cumulonimbus clouds can be very violent in nature. Cumuliform clouds may form individually with clear sky between them or in a continuous line such as in a line squall along a cold front. Precipitation may be heavy but is usually short lived. Airframe icing and turbulence will depend upon the vertical development. Cumulus fractus, simply broken cumulus, can appear as irregular shreds, associated with a large cumulus cloud. They look as though they have been torn from the main body of a cumulus cloud.

Stratiform or layer cloud usually has a low uniform base and is grey in appearance. It can occur in ragged patches, often with layers of clear air between further cloud layers. It seldom produces precipitation, if it does it will be light to moderate drizzle or snow with airframe icing no worse than moderate. Small detached stratus fractus clouds formed below a layer of higher stratiform or nimbostratus cloud are called scud.

Over high ground stratiform clouds form when the air is moist and cools to its dewpoint as it is forced to rise over a range of hills. The hill itself may be totally covered in cloud, and as the cloud is so dense and close to the ground it is called hill fog. When the air flows over the hill and back to lower ground the cloud will warm and disperse.

Stratocumulus is a low cloud. Its base is stratiform in appearance but sometimes with breaks. It is grey in colour with whitish patches or layers and is differentiated from a thick stratus layer by the comparatively uneven tops.

When a stratus cloud has a very grey, dark appearance, often dark enough to blot out the Sun, it is known as nimbostratus. The darkness is caused by the large concentration of water droplets within the cloud. Its passing is usually associated with continuous falling rain or snow.

The most exciting clouds are naturally the most active. They are also the most uncomfortable for the pilot. Moderate cumulonimbus clouds are dark, dense and usually produce virga, (rain or snow that evaporates before reaching the ground) and precipitation. There are many Latin names linked to specific cumulus formations such as cumulonimbus mamma. This is a cumulonimbus cloud that has hanging extensions, likened to pouches or udders, indicative of severe turbulence. These specific types are not described individually as their existence is largely academic. The general term cumulonimbus will cover all the variations.

Well-developed cumulonimbus clouds are more commonly known as thunderstorms. Requirements for a thunderstorm are instability, high moisture and a trigger action. The unstable layer must be at least 10,000 feet in depth and the trigger action can be any form of lifting. This may be convective, frontal or a combination of both. The source of the lift categorises the type of thunderstorm into either an air mass or frontal thunderstorm.

At any time there are approximately 1,800 thunderstorms in progress over the Earth but is unlikely that even in the worst conditions more than 10 will exist over the UK at any one time. For a full-grown thunderstorm to form it must go through three textbook stages of development.

The Development Stage	This is where several small cumulus clouds will combine to form one larger cloud. The base may be more than five miles across. Updrafts suck in air from the base and side of the cloud. This stage lasts approximately thirty minutes.
The Mature Stage	A developed cumulonimbus cloud will be dark in appearance with massive towers that may extend well into the stratosphere. Beneath the base there may be heavy rain or hail (despite the localised temperature) with violent up and down drafts. It is possible for a tornado (or waterspout if the storm passes over water) to be formed. The most violent stage in an individual

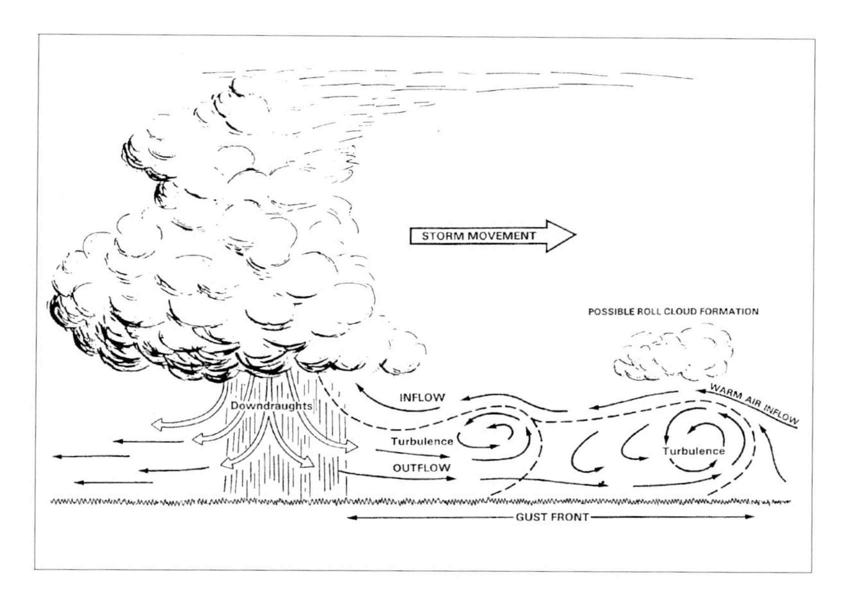

Figure 14.4 The wind flow in the vicinity of a typical thunderstorm.

cloud is unlikely to last more than thirty minutes.

The Dissipating Stage

At this stage the downdrafts become most prevalent throughout the cloud and the updrafts diminish. Any anvil formation will show at its most pronounced as the upper water droplets, by now usually ice crystals, drift downwind in the direction of the prevailing 10,000 feet (700mb) wind. This stage will usually last less than one hour unless it is topped up with further active cumulonimbus clouds.

The advance of a front will cause warm air to be forced upwards causing the formation of thunderstorms. Frontal thunderstorms are usually associated with the line squall of a cold front due to their formation in a line along the front. The line squall may be up to 100 miles long and are most prevalent in winter. They can also occur with the passing of a warm front but most commonly at the point of a warm front occlusion where the warmer air is forced to rise vertically.

The effects of thunderstorms on an aircraft

Thunderstorms have very nasty effects on even the largest aircraft and should be given a wide berth. Severe up and down drafts of comparable intensity, often close to each other, exist within thunderstorms and may reach speeds greater than 3,000 feet per minute. The top of a developing cell has been observed to rise at more than 5,000 feet per minute. The vertical extent of thunderstorms varies but may reach 40,000 feet in temperate latitudes and 60,000 feet in subtropical and tropical regions.

Never attempt to climb to fly over a mature or building thunderstorm. It is unlikely you would live through the experience. Severe turbulence may be encountered in clear air several thousand feet above the tops of active thunderstorm clouds. Also avoid flying over the top of small convective cells whenever possible. These may grow very quickly and produce dramatic turbulence.

It is also very unwise to fly under active cumulonimbus clouds. There may be turbulence, rain, hail, snow or lightning. Technically, lightning is caused by glaciation in the cloud triggering the separation of ions; the positive ions collecting at the top of the cloud, the negative near the base, typically near the -10°C isotherm. This builds until there is a discharge of lightning, audibly accompanied by thunder. This harsh crack and rumbling sound is due to the violent expansion of the gases along the line of the lightning.

Most lightning strikes on aircraft occur at levels where the temperature is between +10°C and -10°C. The lightning flash can temporarily blind a pilot but there is unlikely to be much damage apart from burn marks at the point of entry and exit, although radio aerials are often destroyed. Aside from a general engineering check, a compass swing is a mandatory requirement after a strike. If lightning does strike an aircraft, the magnetic compass should not be relied upon. While flying in thunderstorm areas altimeters and vertical speed indicators may display errors of up to +/- 1,000 feet. Consequently it is essential that ground clearance levels allow for this.

Added effects from a storm may be a low cloud base, poor visibility and possible low level wind shear. Winds caused by the outflow of cold air at the base of a storm cell have been recorded as changing by as much as 80 knots and 90 degrees within a few hundred feet.

High level thunderstorms are often brought to the southern UK by south-easterly winds from the French mainland. They have a short life but each storm tends to generate a new one as it dissipates. If the upper winds are light, the storms appear to circle an area. Air mass thunderstorms are very active cumulonimbus clouds that occur most commonly in the afternoon when insolation is at its peak, especially during a weak depression. Over the sea they may develop from relatively cold air moving over a comparatively warm sea. In either event they may develop in conditions of overcast cloud, where they are referred to as embedded CBs. Under these conditions detecting them visually is impossible.

Microbursts sometimes accompany an active cumulonimbus cloud. These are down currents that can have speeds of several thousand feet a minute and a horizontal movement of 50 to 100 knots. They typically last around ten minutes but cause extreme turbulence and wind shear dangers to aircraft. They occur most often in summer air mass storms in low latitude regions when conditions are dry.

A non-hazardous visual effect of thunderstorms can be caused by a build up of static electricity. This is known as Saint Elmo's Fire and results in purple and green rings of light showing around the nose, wing tips and propeller tips. Although not dangerous in itself it does suggest possible lightning conditions.

Precipitation

Solid and liquid precipitation is classified to enable a common description to be given and understood. The durations are:

Duration	Description
Showers	Sunshine between periods of precipitation
Intermittent	Overcast between periods of precipitation
Continuous	Continuous

For liquids they are:

Droplet Size	Description
0.2mm diameter	Drizzle
2.9mm diameter	Moderate
5.5mm diameter	Heavy

For solids they are:

Title	Description
Sleet	Rain and sleet falling together or snow that melts as it falls
Granular Snow (grains)	Opaque white ice less than 1mm in diameter
Ice Needles	Ice crystals less than 2mm long, needle shaped
Snow	Large combinations of opaque and feathery crystals in complex branched hexagonal shapes
Snow Pellets	Opaque white snow-like structures about 2mm diameter. Crisp, will rebound from a hard surface and break up
Soft Hail	Opaque white round pellets of snow

Snow on the Ground

Title	Description
Dry Snow	Snow that can be blown if loose and if compacted by hand will fall apart
Wet Snow	Snow that if compacted by hand will form a snow-ball
Compacted Snow	Snow that has been compressed and resists further compression. Will break up in lumps if picked up.
Slush	Water saturated snow that can be splattered with a heel and toe motion.

There are situations where precipitation will fall from a cloud but not reach the ground, evaporating back into the atmosphere during its descent. This precipitaton can be water droplets but is more often ice crystals. During its short life it is called virga.

When the water droplets or hailstones within a cloud become too heavy for updrafts to support them they fall, either onto an aircraft below or to the ground. Under normal circumstances, in temperatures above zero, this does not present a difficulty to the pilot. Visibility is not often significantly reduced unless the rain is heavy. Rain, however, can cause problems when temperatures are below zero.

Freezing rain can result during conditions where a cold winter spell is about to be overtaken by an advancing warm front. Rain, falling from the front, passes through the sub-zero air below and becomes supercooled. If it contacts an aircraft it will freeze as clear ice. Droplets reaching the ground freeze, forming a coating of ice on most surfaces, including vegetation, taxiways and runways. At the surface it is called glazed frost. Icing hazards and types are covered in detail in Chapter 12.

Hail is formed when snow or water droplets are continually tossed up and down by the updrafts inside a cumulonimbus cloud. They alternately melt and re-freeze until they become balls of ice that are heavy enough to overcome the up current. In the UK hail is most frequent in the summer when cumulonimbus clouds are at their largest. In equatorial regions, especially mountainous areas, the hailstones can reach the size of a grapefruit. At UK latitudes they are usually pea sized but have been recorded up to the size of golf balls and hail damage to aircraft has been recorded as high as 45,000 feet.

Chapter 15

Winds

The wind is of consummate interest to the pilot. A 40 knot headwind directly down a runway can make any short field landing look professional but on the ground it makes taxying in any other direction than into wind a very precarious operation. The jet stream however, with windspeeds of more than 200 knots, can be a real benefit or hindrance to jet traffic.

In the air, a heading has to be laid off to counter any crosswind and maintain a straight track. Apart from navigational considerations the strength of the wind is irrelevant to an aircraft in flight as it does not experience any wind force on its structure. It merely moves within the parcel of air in which it travels, which itself travels over the surface of the Earth.

On the ground the force of the wind becomes a more serious subject. Its effect on movable objects, or supposedly fixed objects, like tied down aircraft, can be considerable.

In 1805, when all ships were entirely dependent on the wind for movement, the Admiralty considered that having a system of classifying the force of the wind would be useful. Such a scale already existed in a 17th century version by a Charles Tomlinson, which graded winds in strength from one to eight. However, it was down to Rear-Admiral and hydrographer to the Royal Navy, Francis Beaufort, to devise the scale, listed below, which is still in regular use today.

To make it more relevant to pilots, a windsock and aircraft category has been added, effectively making this an aeronautical Beaufort scale. The angle of flight of windsocks has been given for both 7-foot and 14-foot windsocks. Most small airfields have the 7-foot versions. Large international airfields will have the full 14-foot size. The average windspeed has been used for each Beaufort scale in relation to the windsock angle.

Force Description	Effect over Land	Effect on Windsocks & Aircraft	Knots	MPH
0 Calm	Smoke rises vertically	Windsock limp	–	–
1 Light Air	Direction of wind shown by smoke drift, but not by wind vanes	Windsock 12° (7'), 9° (14')	1–3	1–3
2 Light Breeze	Wind felt on face and leaves rustle, wind vane moved by wind	Windsock 30° (7'), 22.5° (14')	4–6	4–7
3 Gentle Breeze	Leaves and small twigs in constant motion; wind extends light flags	Crosswind limit of small light singles Windsock 51° (7'), 38° (14')	7–10	8–12
4 Moderate	Raises dust and loose paper, small branches are moved	Crosswind limit of light singles Windsock 78° (7'), 58° (14')	11–16	13–18
5 Fresh	Small trees in leaf begin to sway; crest wavelets form on inland water	Crosswind limit of light twins Windsock 90° (7'), 83° (14')	17–21	19–24
6 Strong	Large branches in motion; whistling heard in overhead wires; umbrellas usable with difficulty	Light a/c difficult to taxi All windsocks at 90°	22–27	25–31
7 Near Gale	Whole trees in motion; inconvenience felt when walking against wind	Wing walkers needed to move light aircraft. Tie downs strongly recommended	28–33	32–38
8 Gale	Breaks twigs off trees; generally impedes progress	Hangarage recommended. Tie downs essential	34–40	39–46
9 Severe Gale	Slight structural damage occurs (chimney pots and slates are removed)	Tie downs on light aircraft can be dragged	41–47	47–54
10 Storm	Seldom experienced inland; trees uprooted; considerable structural damage occurs	Light aircraft overturned or damaged by debris	48–55	55–63
11 Violent Storm		Widespread Damage	56–63	64–72
12 Hurricane		Widespread Damage	64+	73+

Sir Francis, as he later became, seems to have calculated the scale to allow for the wind's increase in pressure in proportion to the square of the wind speed. Force three averages at 8.5 knots, force five at 18.5 knots, so although the wind speed at force five is only just more than twice that of force three, the pressure is almost five times as great. Lyall Watson, in his book *Heaven's Breath*, produced the following table.* The units of pressure are quoted in kilograms per square metre.

Pressure	**1**	**2**	**3**	**4**	**5**	**6**	**7**	**8**	**9**	**10**	**11**	**12**
Ratio	0.05	0.4	1.3	3.2	6.3	11	18	26	36	50	68	85
Force	1	8	27	64	125	216	343	512	720	1000	1331	1728

* Extract from *Heaven's Breath*, Lyall Watson, reproduced by permission of Hodder & Stoughton Ltd/New English Library Ltd.

Simple arithmetic shows that the pressure increases in these proportions which means that a wind at force 10, though it blows no more than 25 times as fast, exerts 1,000 times as much pressure as a wind at force one. However, the most interesting thing about these figures is that there is a curious relationship between the pressure proportions and the Beaufort numbers. The pressures are precisely the cube of each force number. For instance, force six exerts 216 times the pressure of force one, and 6 x 6 x 6 = 216.

This is more than just a mathematical curiosity. No matter how you calculate wind pressure, and no matter what system it may be acting on, there is always a direct relation between the actual force and the Beaufort number. In other words, if you plot the one against the other on a graph, they produce a beautiful straight line.

Forecasts, actuals and windspeeds passed over the radio won't be given in the Beaufort scale, this is reserved for maritime and TV reports. METAR and SPECI reports are given in knots with the direction that it is blowing *from* in degrees *true*. Most ATC units will pass the wind direction on take-off or landing and this is usually in degrees magnetic.

Some airfields will supply you with the wind direction in degrees true. Under these circumstances when you make your crosswind calculations remember that your landing direction is in degrees magnetic, albeit to the nearest 10°. Variation must be added (or subtracted) from the given wind direction to make it appropriate to your approach. The variation can become very relevant to your crosswind limit. If you have a limit of 15 knots, a 20 knot wind at 50° to your runway heading puts you on the limit. When this wind has variation applied at, for instance 5°, it makes the crosswind 16 knots, over your limit. If the crosswind is near limits, you might want to check with the airfield to clarify how the wind direction is referenced. This can be academic where your precise runway direction is +/- 5° (visual approach runways are numbered to the nearest 10°) and the variation is around the UK's figures, but it can be relevant if you operate an aircraft in other parts of the world.

The radio shipping forecasts, and some TV forecasters, will refer to winds as backing or veering. The shifting of the wind across a specific ground point in the anticlockwise direction is known as backing while a shift in a clockwise direction it is called veering.

CHAPTER 16
THE CAUSES OF WIND

Wind is the movement of air caused by differences of pressure at a given height. The rate of change in pressure with distance is known as the pressure gradient and is measured in millibars (mb) or hectopascals (hPa) per kilometre. Isobars, lines on a synoptic chart that join points of equal barometric pressure, are used to illustrate where bands of pressure lie. If isobars are plotted close together, a steep pressure gradient exists, if they are widely spaced the gradient is slack.

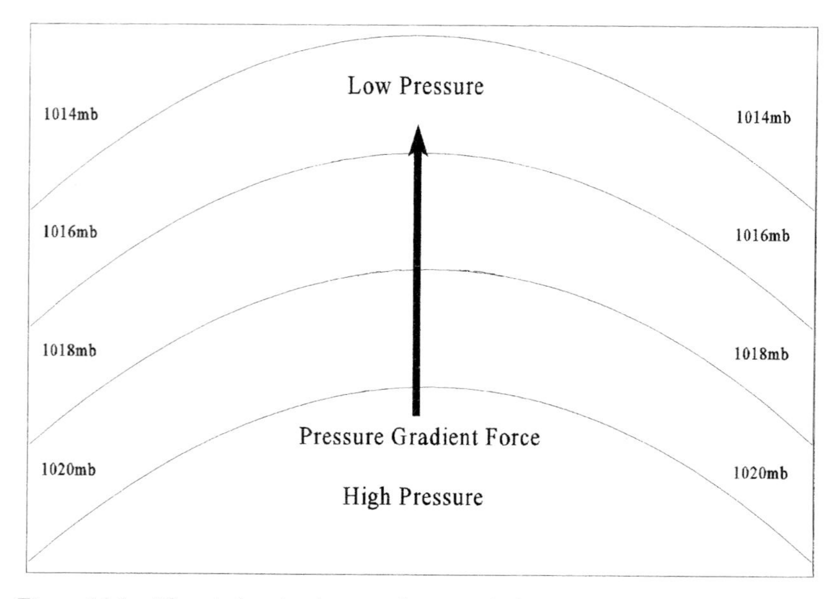

Figure 16.1 The wind acting in accordance with the pressure gradient force which only remains true for equatorial regions.

The movement from high to low should, at first thought, be straightforward. Just as a puncture in a car tyre will quickly result in the equalisation of pressure from inside to out. However, the Earth's air masses are affected by the rotation of the planet, an action known as the Coriolis Effect.

Air tries to move from high pressure to low horizontally as it attempts to equalise atmospheric pressure. However, movement over a distance of more than a few kilometres is affected by the Coriolis Effect. In the northern hemisphere the effect deflects movement to the right, south of the equator it is deflected to the left. Another phenomenon caused by the Coriolis Effect is where water spirals down the plughole clockwise in the northern hemisphere and anticlockwise in the southern. On the equator it simply goes down the plughole without a spiral.

As latitude increases so does the Coriolis force. The Effect has less influence on air movements near the equator and there is no geostrophic wind within 15° of this point where all movements flow with the pressure gradient.

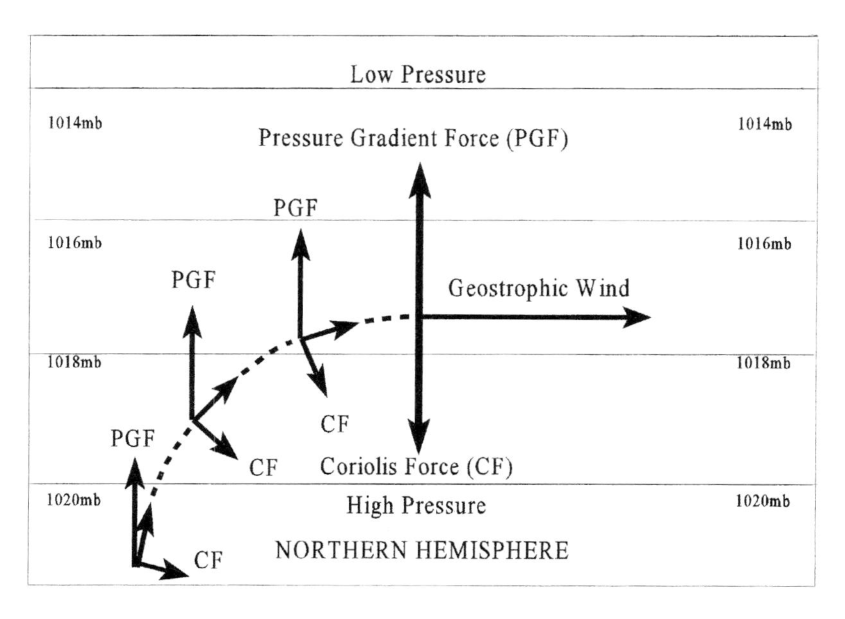

Figure 16.2 The Corolis force acting on the pressure gradient wind at 90° and modifying it until it flows parallel to the (theoretical) straight isobars.

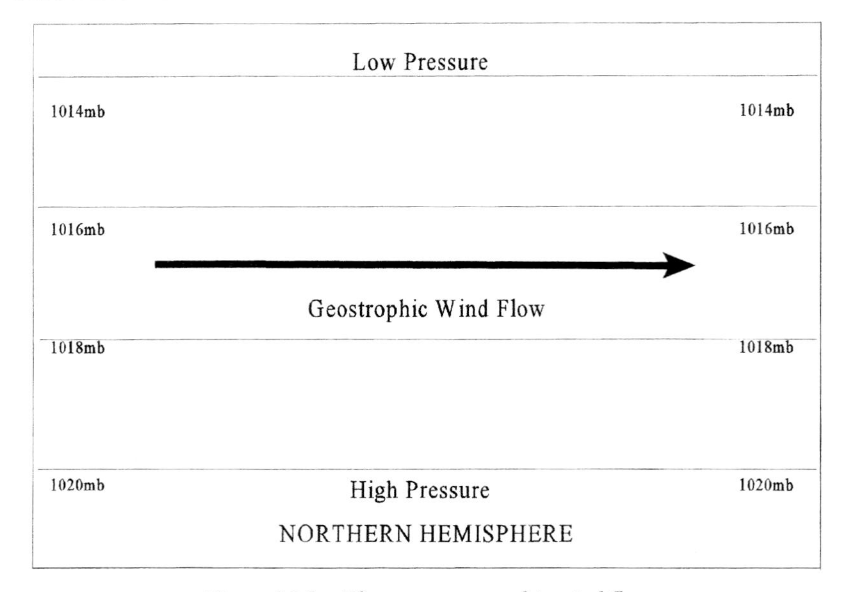

Figure 16.3 The pure geostrophic wind flow.

The Coriolis Effect acts on the pressure gradient wind flow at 90° and results in the formation of a wind that flows parallel to the isobars. This movement is called the geostrophic wind and is taken to mean the flow of air at around 2,000 feet above the surface, measured away from turbulence caused by ground features.

The pure *geostrophic wind* theoretically exists only when isobars are straight and parallel. In reality isobars are in the main curved, and for the wind to follow the curves an additional force is required. This is the centrifugal force and its action varies dependent on whether it is acting around a high or low pressure system.

The forces involved to create a true wind direction are the pressure gradient force that acts at right angles to the isobars, friction that acts in the direction opposite to the direction of the wind (mainly in the bottom 2,000 feet of the atmosphere) and, if the airflow is not in a straight line, centripetal force (v^2 / r where r is the radius of curvature of the flow).

When all the forces are involved, the *gradient wind* is produced. In

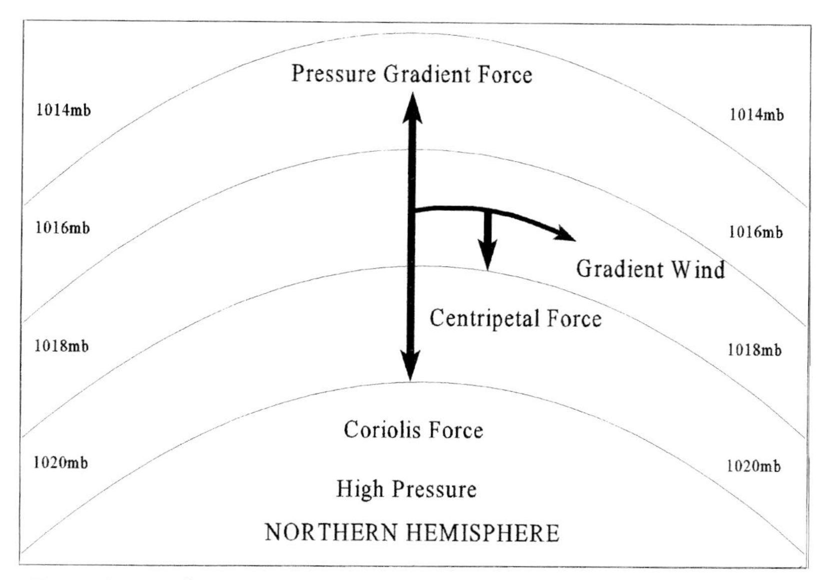

Figure 16.4 The centripetal force (for isobars curved around a high pressure system) acting on the geostrophic wind and forcing it to flow parallel to the curved isobars.

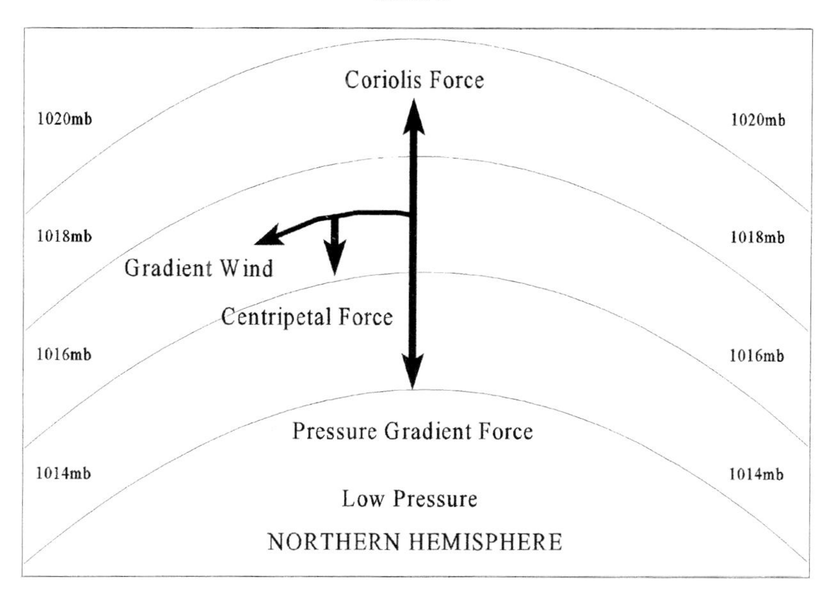

Figure 16.5 The centripetal force (for isobars curved around a low pressure system) acting on the geostrophic wind and forcing it to flow parallel to the curved isobars.

an area of cyclonically curved flow the centrifugal force acts to reduce the geostrophic wind and, around anticyclonically curved isobars, they act together to increase the wind and in the extreme, double it.

Friction slows the wind in the *boundary layer* so that it blows across the isobars at an angle between about 10° and 30°. Unless compensated for at high levels, this will cause anticyclones to lose pressure (decline) and will add pressure to depressions (fill). Friction is a lot more important over land than the sea, and mountains can affect airflow in regions many times their own height.

Buys Ballot's Law

Buys Ballot's Law states: *If an observer in the northern hemisphere stands with his back to the wind then the low pressure will be on his left.* This relates to the wind at approximately 2,000 feet above the surface, so it is free from the drag of surface friction but the height varies dependent on the type of ground surface. It proves that in the northern hemisphere the wind blows parallel to the isobars and circulates anticlockwise around a low and clockwise round a high. The opposite applies in the southern hemisphere.

Thermal winds also behave according to this law with the modification that the area of low temperature will lie to the left, the high temperature to the right.

Specific Wind Types, and their causes

Isallobaric Wind

An isallobaric wind component is the term used to describe the inertial effect caused by a pressure gradient of such strength that it delays the effect of the geostrophic force. The effect in an area of low pressure will be that air will converge towards the centre of pressure; due to this accumulation some air will be forced upwards, resulting in adiabatic cooling and condensation. The effect on an area of high pressure will be that air will move away from the centre causing adiabatic heating and evaporation, dispersing any cloud. The isallobaric wind is most marked when there is a rapid fall in pressure in an area where the original air speed is light. The wind direction can swing 45° or more towards the low pressure area before the Coriolis Effect and centripetal force eventually modify it to flow parallel to the isobars.

Thermal Wind

In the northern hemisphere the thermal wind component flows parallel to the isotherms with the low pressure system to the left. An isotherm is the term used to describe a line that joins points of equal temperature. Thermal wind results from the temperature difference between two air masses and is proportional to the temperature gradient. It is possible for two air masses to have similar pressures but differing temperatures where the air will flow from warm to cold and be affected by the Coriolis Effect, deflecting it to the right in the northern hemisphere. Jet streams, found in the upper atmosphere, result from the thermal gradient.

Cyclone

The word cyclone is normally used to denote a low pressure weather system or depression. The word is misused to denote a tornado, or, in latitudes around the tropical oceans, to describe a tropical cyclone, hurricane or typhoon. The official classification of tropical cyclones for the north Atlantic and eastern north Pacific regions are:

Winds up to 34 knots	Tropical Depression
Winds of 35 to 64 knots	Tropical Storm
Winds of 65 knots or more	Hurricane or Typhoon

A cyclone that forms and moves along a front, deforming the line of the front with a wave like cloud formation is known as a wave cyclone.

Lull

Lull is the term used to describe a temporary decrease in wind speed, the opposite is known as a gust. These are usually reported to the pilot when the difference between a gust and a lull is at least 10 knots.

Föhn Wind

Any wind blowing across the surface of the Earth will attempt to find the easiest route. If the route is blocked by a range of mountains or hills, it will attempt to find a valley or ravine that will offer an easier passage rather than go over the top, resulting in a valley wind. If however there is no way round, such as with the French Alps, the air is forced to rise over the mountains and the wind that blows on the leeward side of the mountains is known as a Föhn wind.

The climb and descent greatly affects the moisture content of the air. As the air rises it cools adiabatically at the dry adiabatic lapse rate. If the mountains are sufficiently high, and the air holds enough moisture, it will eventually reach its dewpoint temperature. As the air rises further, condensation will form and further cooling results at the saturated adiabatic lapse rate with extensive cloud and rain covering the windward side.

On reaching the peak, the air will start to descend. It will now be much less moist and, as it descends, warms adiabatically at the saturated adiabatic lapse rate. It will reach its condensation level at a much greater height than on the windward side. As it descends further, it warms at the dry adiabatic lapse rate. The resultant air flowing down the leeward side will be much warmer and drier than the air on the windward side.

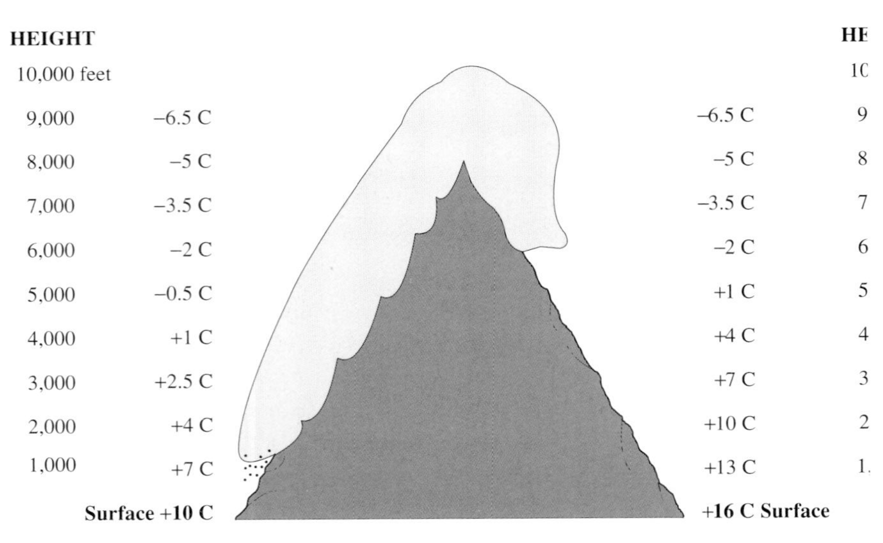

Figure 16.6 An example of a Föhn wind. The air forced to rise cools initially at the dry adiabatic lapse rate and after condensation at the saturated rate. As the air is less moist when it starts its descent the cloud disperses at a higher level and the air warms at the dry rate. The surface temperature difference in this example is 6°C from windward to leeward.

The rate of warming can be as high as 1.5°C for each 1,000 feet of descent. An example of a Föhn wind is where a low pressure system moves across France. As it approaches the Alps it pulls air from the Mediterranean up the southern slopes. As it cools, a line of stratocumulus forms and the dry air flows down the northern slopes. A temperature rise of more than 10°C and fall in relative humidity to 20% results in dramatic weather changes over a very short period.

Katabatic Winds

Katabatic winds are caused by the cooling of a slope where the surface warmth is radiated back into the atmosphere. The air closest to the surface cools faster than the air away from it and being more dense, flows down the slope. This action can result in winds of significant strength even up to gale force. This can present a considerable danger to pilots of aircraft flying towards a mountain area that is experiencing a katabatic wind, especially if the conditions are compounded in a valley. The downdraft might exceed the climb performance of the aircraft. The wind is also known as the drainage wind or mountain breeze.

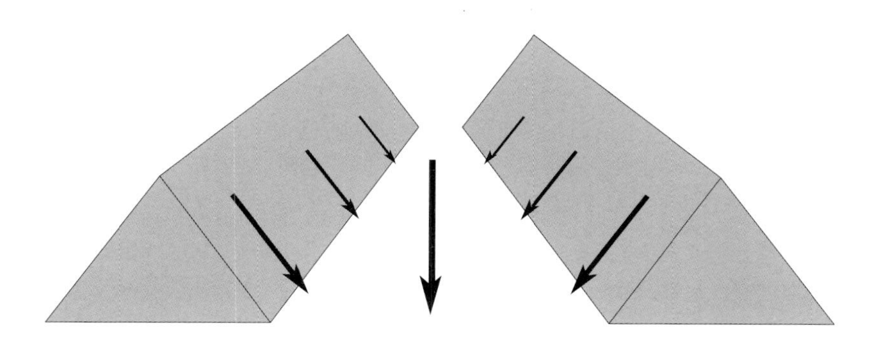

Figure 16.7 Katabatic winds in a valley combining to form a strong downdraft.

Anabatic Winds

Anabatic winds result from solar radiation warming the surface of a slope. As the air close to the surface is warmed, it becomes warmer than the air away from that surface at the same height. This then rises and drifts up the slope. Unlike katabatic winds, anabatic winds are gentle and are seldom of any significance.

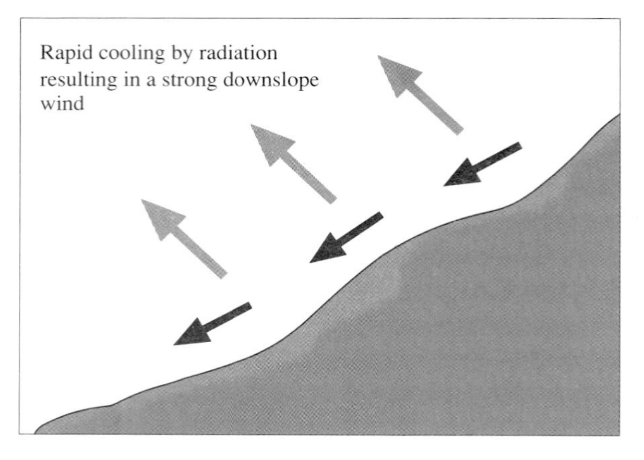

Figure 16.8 Katabatic Winds
Without the Sun's heat the surface cools rapidly, cooling the air next to it. This cold dense air sinks and is replaced by warmer air that is itself cooled. If the slope is steep the wind speed can build up to gale force, exceeding the climb rate of aircraft flying towards the mountain. Airfields near the base of the slope will be kept clear of cloud. Valleys will suffer a build up of dense cold air that often turns to mist or fog in the late afternoon or evening.

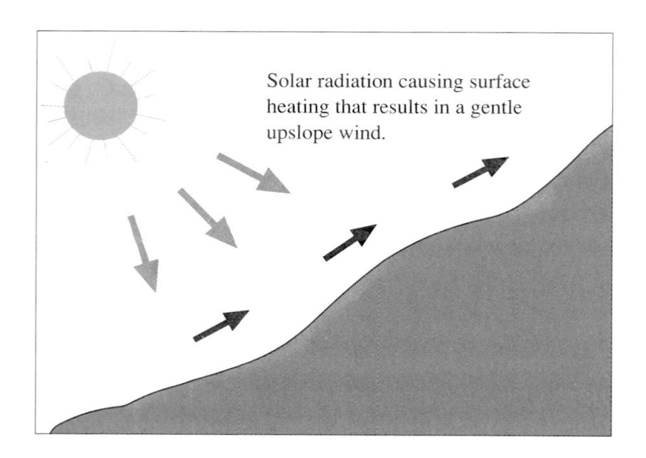

Figure 16.9 Anabatic winds
The Sun's heat warms the sloped surface that in turn warms the air near it. The warmed air rises to be replaced with cooler air which itself is warmed and rises. The process results in a gentle breeze and continues until the surface heating ceases.

If you have trouble remembering the difference between katabatic and anabatic think of acrobats going up on a high wire and kats sleeping on the floor!

Squalls

A squall is the term given to a temporary and sudden increase in wind speed of at least 16 knots, to a peak of 22 knots or more, that lasts at least one minute at the peak speed. Squalls are associated with cold fronts. A shorter increase is known as a gust.

Gusts

A gust is a sudden increase in wind speed, often with a change of direction. Its duration is usually only a few seconds and is only local in nature.

Surface Winds

The geostrophic wind passing over the surface of the Earth is disturbed if it encounters any obstacles. These may take the form of a man-made constructions, natural formations or vegetation. Their effect on the wind flow in the northern hemisphere will be to cause it to slow and back.

The mixing effect of the wind upon meeting surface obstacles results in a vertical wind layer known as the turbulence layer or friction layer. The friction layer is affected by the wind strength and by the amount of surface heating. Surface heating results in thermal turbulence caused by the effect of warmed air rising away from the surface. The strength of the wind as it encounters an obstacle relates to the amount of turbulence and is known as mechanical turbulence.

A friction layer is judged to be thick or thin in comparison with the 2,000 feet geostrophic wind. The thicker the friction layer the less difference there will be between the surface wind and the geostrophic wind. Friction layers will exhibit predictable diurnal variations. At night when there is no thermal turbulence the friction layer will be at its thinnest. A surface wind, when quoted by ATC will be that measured at a height of 10 metres by an anemometer located in an area free of obstructions.

Valley Winds

The term valley wind is often used to describe an anabatic wind. Alternatively it is used to describe a ravine wind. Any wind blowing across the surface of the Earth will attempt to find the easiest route. If the route is blocked by a range of mountains or hills, it will flow around rather than over it. To effect this detour it will change direction significantly to find a valley or ravine. The air entering this constriction will then have to increase its speed (known as funnelling) and can cause severe localised effects. Any minor veering or backing of the wind approaching the obstruction can, if the angles are critical, cause a complete reversal of the direction of the ravine wind.

Mountain Waves

Mountain waves are also known as standing waves or lee waves. As the name implies, this refers to air wave formations that are effectively static in position in relation to the mountain. For these waves to be created certain criteria are required. A range of mountains sloping on the windward side, steep on the leeward side, and a wind of constant direction blowing within 30° of the face of the range. The windspeed must be at least 15 knots and increasing with height.

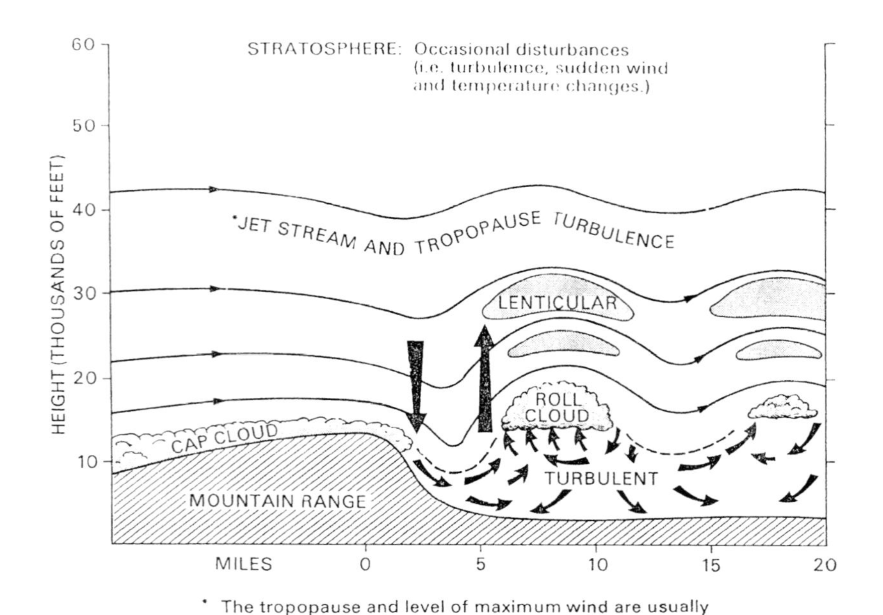

Figure 16.10 The typical features of a mountain wave

Finally, a stable layer of air just above the summit of the range with layers of unstable air above and below is required. If no clouds are present standing waves will be impossible to detect visually. The waves will influence the area downwind by up to 250 miles and from the surface to 30,000 feet in extreme cases. The wavelength of a standing wave is usually between two and 20 miles. The waves often produce cloud types that clearly mark the areas of activity.

Cap clouds can cover the windward side and peak of the mountains and are created by the same process as Föhn winds and lenticular clouds. These appear stationary in the stable air at the peak of each wave and may occur at various heights. The high liquid content held in these clouds may cause severe icing. Roll cloud may also be found below the peak on the leeward side. This cloud is created by extreme up and downdrafts known as rotor zones and will mark the area of most turbulence. If there are strong surface winds, rotor zones may flow downwind causing rotor streaming.

Sea Breezes

Sea breezes at UK latitudes have a very localised effect, rarely extending more than 20 miles inland and 1,500 feet vertically. The

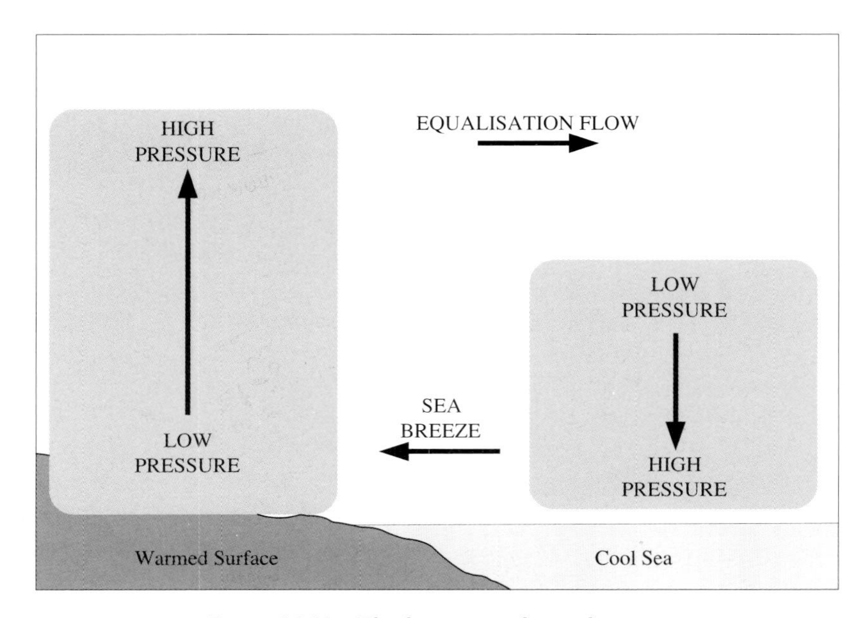

Figure 16.11 The formation of a sea breeze.

wind strength will not normally exceed 10 knots. The breeze is a result of the difference in surface heating of land in comparison to water. The sea temperature remains almost constant even when solar radiation is at its diurnal peak. The daily land temperatures can vary dramatically (consider the sand on a continental beach after midday and that at dawn).

Sea breezes are most prolific when a slack pressure gradient is present and cloud cover is minimal. The cycle starts after dawn when solar radiation begins to warm the Earth's surface, the air in contact with this is warmed and rises. This causes the geostrophic (2,000 feet) pressure to rise and drift towards the area of lower pressure that is now over the sea. As the cycle continues, the high pressure flow begins to build over the sea leaving a low pressure area over the land. Surface air now flows from the sea to the land where it is heated and the cycle continues. Sea breezes established for a few hours are affected by the Coriolis force deflecting the flow to the right so that the wind blows round the heat low instead of into it. The reverse effect of a sea breeze that occurs at sunset is called a land breeze.

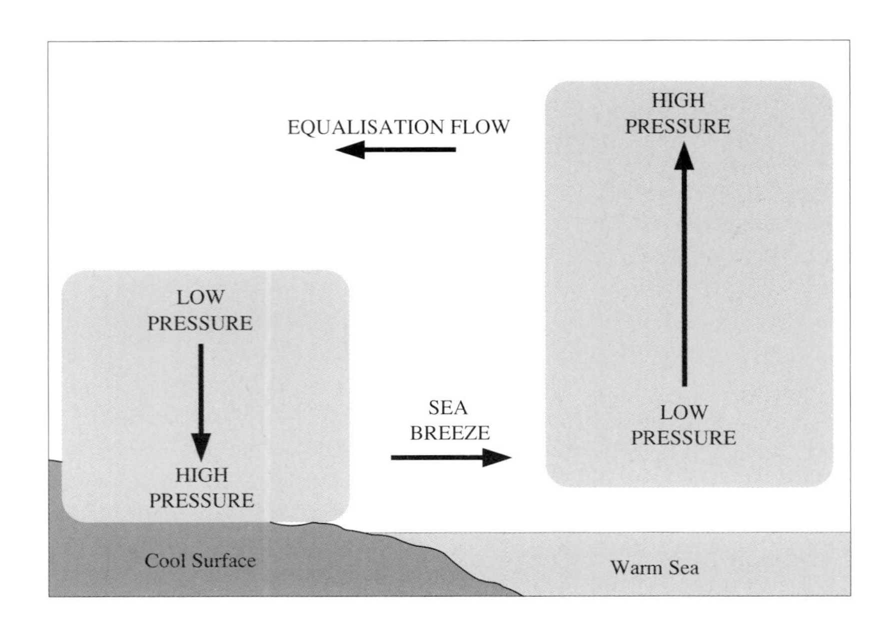

Figure 16.12 The formation of a land breeze.

Land Breezes

A land breeze may form after sunset when the Earth's surface becomes cooler than that of the sea. It causes a drift of air from land to sea and is the opposite of the cycle of events that cause a sea breeze (see figure 16.12).

Wind shear

Wind shear is the change of wind direction and/or speed over a short distance. These variations may be vertical, horizontal or a combination of both. The most severe wind shear is associated with thunderstorms but may also coincide with the passage of a front.

Thunderstorms tend to have an area of cold air that causes a down draught in all directions but which is often well marked along the line of its movement. This is known as a gust front. This area may extend up to a height of 6,000 feet and 20 miles ahead of the centre of the storm. Frontal wind shear occurs in active fronts that are moving at speeds of more than 30 knots and where there are large temperature differences.

Low level wind shear is a particular hazard to aircraft during the take-off or landing phases of a flight. Take for example a case where wind shear is horizontal and the wind speed on the distant side of the shear line is 20 knots lower than the side containing a landing aircraft. If the aircraft approaches at 130 knots air speed, this indicated air speed will reduce to 110 knots as it passes through the line. The aircraft may be placed within its stall envelope.

If the shear is purely vertical and a downdraft, the angle of attack can effectively be changed at the instant it passes through the shear line. If the shear line variation has a combined vertical and horizontal component it can critically affect an aircraft's approach or take-off.

Tornadoes

Tornadoes are intense vortices of circulating air that lower towards the surface as funnel clouds. They are micro-systems which have a very low pressure at the centre surrounded by extremely strong winds. A tornado will average 100 miles in diameter and can, in extreme cases, create wind speeds of 200 knots. The base of the tornado does not always reach the ground; if it does it will suck up any loose debris in its path. If a tornado occurs over the sea, it is then referred to as a waterspout.

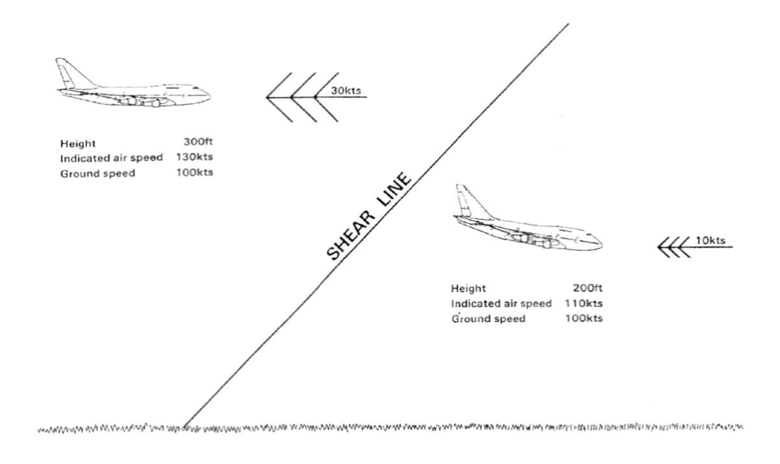

Figure 16.13 The loss of indicated airspeed when passing through a shear line with a reduced windspeed on the far side.

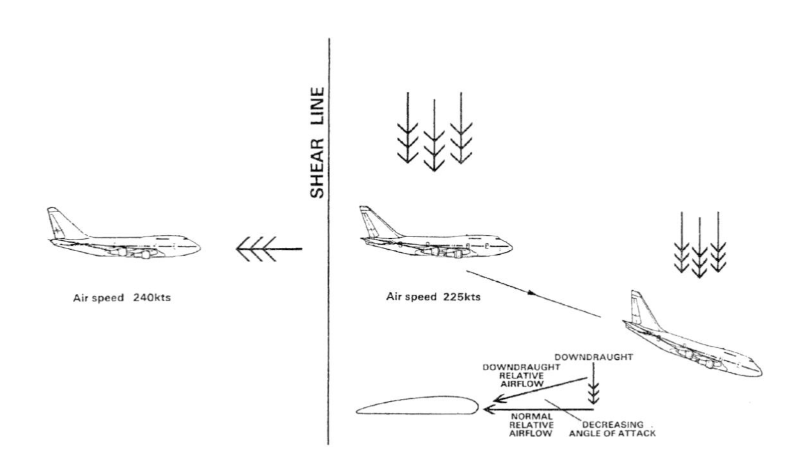

Figure 16.14 The effect of a downdraft when passing through a vertical shear line.

Jet Streams

Jet streams are created when the thermal gradient is large. They are tubes of fast moving thermal wind, thousands of miles in length, hundreds of miles in width and a few miles in depth. They occur near the tropopause where there is a substantial difference in temperature over a very small distance and result from the air's attempt to equalise the differential. Within a jet stream, windspeeds can exceed 200 knots

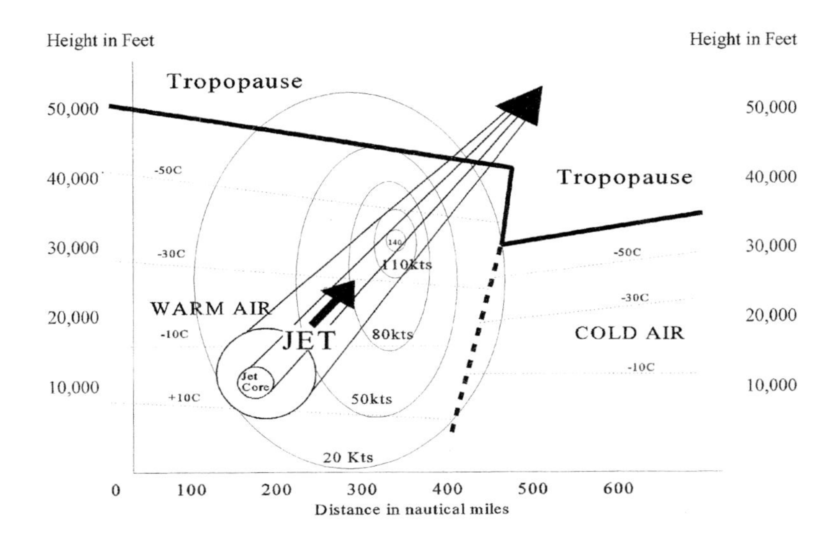

Figure 16.15 The formation of a jet stream.

There are two main types, polar front and subtropical. The polar front jet stream varies in position from day to day and over a wide range of latitudes. The subtropical jet stream remains relatively constant in position dependent on the season.

Jet stream activity, and the resultant clear air turbulence, will only affect the heights used by pressurised aircraft and can cause fuel and flight time estimate problems if encountered unexpectedly. Clear air turbulence can be uncomfortable and hazardous as detecting it in advance is impossible, either visually or on radar. The only advance indications will be sudden changes in wind direction and temperature. Turbulence is classified as follows:

Light	Causing slight, rapid, rhythmic bumpiness without changes in altitude, attitude or indicated air speed.
Moderate	As light turbulence but more pronounced with changes in altitude, attitude and indicated air speed. Indicated air speed fluctuations of up to 25 knots. Aircraft controllable.
Severe	Extensive, abrupt changes in altitude and attitude resulting in the aircraft being out of control temporarily. Air speed indications fluctuating more than 25 knots.

Chapter 17

Weather Reports, Charts and Forecasts

A personal briefing with a qualified meteorologist can still be obtained in some countries but the UK has opted for the self-briefing system. This means that at aerodromes where a Met office is located, all the information regarding the actual and forecast weather will be provided. All the pilot has to do is interpret it!

With the innovations of the fax machine, all this data can be obtained via the METFAX system. This system is covered later in this chapter, but first let us cover the main items available from the average airfield's briefing room.

The METAR

A METAR is more commonly called an actual, abbreviated from a meteorological aerodrome report, and is used to state the observed weather at specific aerodromes. It must be taken into account that there is a time lag between the observation times and the period taken to get the reports in front of you. They are compiled at half-hourly or hourly intervals and a further period is taken before they are issued. Full details of a METAR decode are given in the yellow section of the *Aeronautical Information Circulars* AIC 110/1995 (Yellow 199) and amendments in AIC 14/1996 (Yellow 207), but a METAR will always take the following form:

Location Identifier
The ICAO four letter code for an aerodrome.

Time

The time of observation in hours and minutes followed by the letter Z for Zulu Time that is a synonym for UTC (universal coordinated time).

Wind

The direction in degrees true, from the direction that the wind is flowing. This is followed by the measuring unit, usually KT for knots but could be KMH, kilometres per hour or MPS, metres per second. If the letter G follows, it means gusting. This is followed by the maximum expected gust speed. It is only given if the gust is expected to exceed the mean speed by 10 knots or more. VRB stands for variable and is given for light wind conditions. Calm is shown as 00000. If the wind direction varies by more than 60° in the 10 minute period before the observation time the two extremes will be quoted, providing the wind speed is greater than three knots. Then the two directions are separated by V. For example 190V270.

Horizontal Visibility

The visibility is given in metres. 9999 means visibility greater than 10km. If the visibility varies significantly in different directions, the variants are shown by use of the eight points of the compass. Mist, haze, smoke, diamond dust (ice crystals), dust and sand are not reported unless the phenomena reduces visibility to less than 5,000 metres, or 3,000 in respect of mist.

Runway Visual Range

R denotes runway followed by the runway number. If it is then followed by R C or L it denotes right, centre or left runway. This will usually be followed by /P1500 which means that the RVR is in excess or 1,500 metres. If the information given is other than /P1500 it is likely that the visibility is unsuitable for a non-IMC or Instrument rated pilot. RVR decodes are given in the MET Section of the *Air Pilot*.

Weather

Indications will follow some logic for example: SHRA, showers of rain; +BLSN, heavy blowing snow. Qualifiers are used to indicate its intensity or proximity: (-) light, moderate, (+) heavy or VC meaning in the vicinity (within 8km of an aerodrome perimeter but not at the aerodrome itself).

Cloud
Cloud will be given as FEW for one to two oktas, SCT – Scattered, indicating three to four oktas. BKN – Broken, indicating five to seven oktas or OVC – Overcast verifying eight oktas. This is followed by the height of the base of cloud in hundreds of feet above aerodrome level. If the sky is obscured the code VV is followed by the vertical visibility. If that cannot be measured VV/// is quoted. If cumulonimbus or towering cumulus clouds are in the area an abbreviation will be placed after the cloud height. If there is no cloud the abbreviation CAVOK may be added to a report TREND (see below for TRENDS), if this cannot apply SKC, meaning sky clear is used.

Temperature/Dewpoint
Given in degrees centigrade, M indicates minus.

QNH
Rounded down to the nearest whole millibar and reported as a four-figure group preceded by the letter Q, if the value is less than 1,000 the first digit is shown as a 0. When it is reported in inches of mercury, it is prefixed by A.

Recent Weather
The type of operationally significant recent weather will be given if it has passed since the previous observation, or in the last hour (whichever is shorter). This is given the prefix RE.

Wind shear
Prefixed WS, followed by the runway affected. It will be included if wind shear has been reported up to 1,600 ft above the runway elevation along the take-off or approach paths.

Trend
This will indicate significant changes (or lack of them) during the two hours after the observation time. Specific types of trend are explained on page 129.

Runway State
This is only added to the end of the METAR (or SPECI) if the runway is affected by snow or other contamination. This takes the form of an eight-figure group. The first two figures designate which runway is affected: 26 means runway 26 or by default, 26 left if there are two; 50 is added to the figure if it relates to the right runway. Therefore if it were 26 right the figure 76 would be given. If the figure is 88, it means the data applies to all runways and 99 means that the last report is repeated as no new information has been received.

The third figure relates to the type of runway contamination: 0 = clear and dry, 1 = damp, 2 = wet or water patches, 3 = rime ice or frost covered, 4 = dry snow, 5 = wet snow, 6 = slush, 7 = ice, 8 = compacted or rolled snow, 9 = frozen ruts or ridges and / means no current report is available.

The extent of runway contamination is shown by the fourth figure: 1 = 10% or less, 2 = 11% to 25%, 5 = 26% to 50%, 9 = 51% to 100% and / means that no report is currently available.

If the runway is contaminated by snow, an average depth is measured or, if significant, the greatest depth. These figures are coded by the fifth and sixth figures: 00 = less than 1mm, 01 to 90 gives the actual depth in mm. The numbers 92 to 98 are used to denote 10cm or more in 5cm increments, for example 95 means 25cm: 99 means the runway is closed due to snow and // that the covering is not significant or has not been measured.

The final two-figure group gives the friction coefficient or braking action: 25 indicates a braking coefficient of 0.25, 30 means 0.30, 91 = braking action poor, 92 = medium/poor, 93 = medium/good and 95 good.

If the runway is cleared, the letters CLRD will replace the middle four figures and the braking action report will still be given.

Any information that is missing from a METAR will be shown by diagonals or slashes (///).

If the METAR is issued by a military airfield the report may be followed by a colour code, BLU for blue, GRN for green etc. A full list of these colour codes is given on page 138.

CAVOK

Derived from ceiling and visibility OK. Meteorologically it means that the visibility is 10km or more, no cloud below 5,000ft or below the highest minimum sector altitude, whichever is the greater, and no cumulonimbus. It also means that there is no significant weather at or in the vicinity of the airfield.

Having absorbed that lot, do not rush off to the airfield expecting the best flying day this year. On most occasions the sight of CAVOK on the METAR will mean great VMC flying but read this information with all the other data. Conditions could deteriorate within two hours from CAVOK to a visibility of 6km and/or a ceiling of 1,600ft without the TREND being considered incorrect. The criteria for significant changes for TREND type forecasts are given in Table K of the MET Section of the UK AIP.

Trend

A trend is a short term landing forecast valid for two hours after the observation time and added to a METAR or VOLMET. It is used to add a forecast to the end of an actual and will be in one of the following forms prefixed by the word TREND:

BECMG	Becoming
INTER	Intermittent changes with conditions fluctuating
NOSIG	No significant changes expected
PROB	Percentage of probability of a change occurring
RAPID	Rapid change occurring in ½ hour or less
TEMPO	Change expected to last for less than one hour

Terminal Aerodrome Forecast – TAF

TAFs are prepared between one and two hours before the start of the period of validity. This period should be allowed for when considering their accuracy. For civil aerodromes they are valid for either a nine or 18-hour period. The nine-hour TAFs are updated every three hours, the 18-hour, every six hours.

Both have routine issue times: 0100 hrs UTC for nine-hour and 0600 hrs UTC for the 18-hour. Full details of a TAF decode are given in AIC 14/1996 (Yellow 207) and they are the same as for METARs with a few exceptions:

Multi-use

If a TAF consists of forecasts for more than one aerodrome, the code name TAF will be replaced by FC or FT.

Validity Time

The hours of validity, from and to, in UTC.

Horizontal Visibility

The same as a METAR except that only the minimum value will be given.

Weather

If there is no significant weather the section will be left out. If there is weather at the start of the TAF, and after a change no significant weather is expected, the code NSW will be given. Forecast clear skies are shown by SKC. If that and CAVOK are not appropriate then no significant cloud will be indicated by NSC, which means no cumulonimbus and no cloud below 5,000 feet or the Minimum Sector Altitude.

Probability

Forecasters always aim on the safe side and suggest the worst conditions that are likely to occur. If they consider the chances of a set of circumstances being less than 30%, it is ignored. If it's around 50% it will be included in the forecast. A 30% or 40% chance will be shown as a probability, abbreviated to PROB, but bear in mind that is still a 70% or 60% improbability.

Runway Visual Range
Not shown in a TAF as it is never forecast, it's too critical and variable to predict.

Forecast Temperature
Given on some overseas and UK Military TAFs but not general UK aerodromes.

Airframe Ice Accretion and Turbulence
For decode information refer to AIC 110/1995 (Yellow 199) and amendments in AIC 14/1996 (Yellow 207).

Spot Wind Charts – Metform 214

Spot wind charts are issued by the UK Meteorological Office at Bracknell. The chart shows the time of issue and validity. The boxes overlaid on the chart itself are placed at intersections of meridians and parallels. This is the principal aid to cross-country route planning.

The aircraft's route should be drawn on to the chart and the nearest box used to calculate the heading. If the track passes between two boxes then the average of the two should be used. The charts are issued at the following times, UTC:

Fixed time validity	Suitable for flights within the periods	Charts available at
0300	0000 – 0600	2300
0800	0600 – 1100	0500
1200	1000 – 1500	0900
1600	1400 – 1900	1300
2100	1800 – 2400	1700

Area Forecasts – Metform 215

The low level area and route forecast is issued by the Meteorological Office at Bracknell. It covers the same area as the Metform 214 and so they are normally used together. The sheet shows, both pictorially and in text, the expected flight conditions from the surface to 15,000 feet. The period of validity is shown on the top left, the time and date of issue, bottom right. A full decode and explanation of symbols is given on Metform 216. The charts are issued at fixed times and cover standard periods:

Fixed time validity	Suitable for initial departures and flights between	Charts available at
0800	0600 – 1100	0500
1200	1000 – 1500	0900
1600	1400 – 1900	1300
2100	1800 – 2400	1700
0300	0000 – 0600	2300

Other sources of forecasts and actual weather . . .

Broadcast FAX and MIST

Broadcast FAX and MIST services are provided by the Met Office for aviation organisations and airfield briefing rooms and beyond the requirements (and pocket) of most private pilots. Details of Broadcast FAX (& METFAX) can be found in AIC 95/1994 (Yellow 161).

METFAX

METFAX is the ultimate simplistic innovation for the private pilot. Providing you have access to a fax machine you can complete all your flight planning before leaving home. The data is provided by the Meteorological Office, Bracknell. The system allows access to all the charts and forecasts, including TAFs and METARs that are available in self briefing met offices at the larger airfields. Telephone charges are at premium rates but when compared with the cost of a flight they pale into insignificance. The index page can be obtained on 0336 400 501 and gives details of all the data available. For advance planning the surface T+48, T+72 forecast chart and three day planning text will give you an idea of the forthcoming weather. On the day of the flight the forecast 214 and 215 charts should be obtained with the METAR and TAFS over the planned route.

As a one-off, it may be worth checking out most of the charts that you think may be of use. This will enable you to assemble your own preferred briefing list. The satellite observations are very dramatic but of little practical value for the average private flight.

Meteorological Forecast – Personalised

Although self-briefings are available from most larger aerodromes, a personalised meteorological forecast (not briefing) can be available if the appropriate notice is given; four hours for flights of 500nm or more, two hours otherwise. They can take some work out of flights to the European mainland and are, currently, free of charge. The initial request should be made to a main or subsidiary meteorology office. If the pilot cannot appear personally at the office, arrangements may be made for the information to be passed by telephone or fax.

The forecast does not alleviate the pilot of the need to self brief for the route as normal. The following information, when appropriate, will be provided for a given period:

Information Supplied	European Route Route	North Atlantic Route
Significant Weather Chart	Yes	Yes
Isotach* Charts for Appropriate Levels	No	Yes
Upper Spot Winds and Temperatures	Yes	No
Tropopause Charts	No	Yes
Maximum Wind Charts	No	Yes
0° Isotherm Levels in 1,000s feet	Yes	No
Aerodrome Forecasts including Alternates	Yes	Yes

* An Isotach is a line joining points of equal wind speed

AIRMET

AIRMET is an automated telephone system giving the pilot access to METAR and TAF information for various airfields. Forecasts are renewed four times a day and become available about half an hour before the period of validity. They cover UK Civil and Military airfields as well as a selection of those on the Continent. Telephone charges are at a premium rate. Further details can be found in AIC 92/1994 (Yellow 159).

Automatic Terminal Information Service – ATIS

ATIS is a recorded message updated by ATC to avoid the same weather information being repeated to approaching or departing pilots and congesting the Approach or Tower frequencies. The ATIS may provide arrival, departure or a combined information service and is either on a discrete frequency or a VOR frequency if it is located at the airfield.

An arrival ATIS contains:

a) Weather reports for the aerodrome.
b) Runway in use, QNH, QFE and details of approach aids in use.
c) Un-serviceability of navigation aids or runways.
d) Any other relevant information.

A departure ATIS contains:

a) Aerodrome QNH.
b) Magnetic surface wind direction and speed.
c) Temperature and dewpoint.
d) Departure runway.
e) Details of un-serviceability of runways or navigation aids.
f) Any other relevant information.

The information is prefixed by a letter of the alphabet that relates to the currency of the information. This letter should be quoted to ATC with your initial contact call. For example *Cardiff Approach this is G-GWYN with information Juliet.* If you happen to have caught the transmission just before it had been changed ATC will normally advise you of the fact and quote any significant changes.

Significant Meteorological Information – SIGMET
A SIGMET is a warning message passed by ATC to aircraft at subsonic cruising levels liable to be affected by meteorological conditions of one or more of the following:

a) Active thunderstorms.
b) Heavy hail.
c) Marked mountain wave activity.
d) Tropical revolving storms.
e) Severe airframe icing.
f) Severe line squalls (50kt +).
g) Severe turbulence.
h) Dust storms/sandstorms that reduce visibility to less than 3 miles.

At transonic and supersonic levels warning messages are sent in respect of:

a) Cumulus Cloud.
b) Hail.
c) Moderate or severe turbulence.

For aircraft approaching or in the vicinity of an aerodrome the following warning will be given:
Fog - when visibility is expected to fall below 1,000 metres.
For aircraft on the ground:
Strong wind warning – when gales (35kt +) gusts (43kt), squalls or snow are imminent.

AIREP
An AIREP is a meteorological message in the other direction; in this case, from air to ground. These tend to be given on a prearranged basis by specific flights and will not normally concern the non-commercial pilot. Small aerodromes without a met unit may ask any approaching or departing flight for the cloud base or tops. This information should be passed in plain English.

SPECI

SPECI is a prefix code for meteorological information reporting of sudden weather changes likely to affect aircraft.

SNOWTAM

Snow clearance plans (SNOPLAN) are issued annually by Class II NOTAM for each airfield. They are plans that are ready to be put into effect if weather conditions warrant it. The plan for each airfield contains:

a) The equipment held and the type of clearance.
b) Height and distance of snow bank if permitted (regarding wing height clearances).
c) Contact authority for current information.
d) Any local deviation from standard practice.

If snow does affect an airfield a SNOWTAM is issued. If snow forces an airfield to close, a SNOCLO message will be added to VOLMET and OPMET messages. The pilot will also be advised of the braking action by ATC or by OPMET.

A SNOWTAM is issued every 24 hours or when a significant change occurs. Runway conditions are reassessed every half hour. The reports take a standard format with depth and condition of precipitation and its effect on runway braking action.

The priorities for snow clearance are: -

1. Main Runway
2. Run Up Areas
3. Aprons
4. Taxiways
5. Airport Roads

Runway braking action is measured by a Mu-meter contained within a friction measuring trailer that will verify the possibility of slush-planing when it indicates a low coefficient of friction. Braking action is not assessed in slush-planing conditions. A Tapley meter is used to assess braking action on ice and dry snow. Information is passed to the pilot in the following form:

Type of Precipitation	Report	Categories
Snow	Braking	Good, Medium good, Medium, Medium Poor, Poor
Snow	Density	Dry, Wet, Compressed, Slush, Standing water
Water	Braking	Good, Medium, Poor
Water	Quantity	Damp, Wet, Water patches, Flooded.
Snow Banks	Only passed if they exceed the height outlined in the SNOPLAN	

Any runway contamination greater than 3mm of water, slush or wet snow, or 10mm of dry snow is likely to affect the aircraft's performance. This is not simply from the increased drag effect on wheels and areas impacting the spray, but also from possible power loss or malfunction due to spray saturation. On landing, aircraft will suffer reduced braking performance and possible aquaplaning that can result in directional control problems. Take-off should not be attempted if the depth of water, slush or wet snow is greater than 15mm or dry snow depth is greater than 60mm. Even very dry powdery snow depths greater than 80mm should mean an extended stopover in the club bar.

Very High Frequency Meteorological Report - VOLMET

VOLMET is a service produced on VHF frequencies to cover weather for selected aerodromes. Other services exist on HF frequencies but this text is restricted to the VHF service. Each VOLMET broadcast cycle is preceded by a time announcement. This time was the time at the end of the observing period. Individual reports are broadcast for 30 minutes after observation. The same report may be continued for a further 30 minutes if no fresh observation has been reported in that period. At the end of one hour, if no up-to-date report is available the report will be suspended. All VOLMET transmissions operate on a 24-hour basis and the UK services are in four sections, these are:

Call Sign	Frequency	Stations Covered
London - Main	135.375	Amsterdam, Brussels, Dublin, Glasgow, London (Gatwick, Heathrow & Stansted), Manchester & Paris (Charles de Gaulle)
London - South	128.600	Birmingham, Bournemouth, Bristol, Cardiff, Jersey, Luton, Norwich, Southampton & Southend
London - North	126.600	Blackpool, East Midlands, Leeds Bradford, Liverpool, London (Gatwick), Manchester, Newcastle, Ronaldsway & Teesside
Scottish	125.725	Aberdeen Dyce, Belfast Aldergrove, Edinburgh, Inverness, London (Heathrow), Prestwick, Stornaway & Sumburgh

The content of the VOLMET is:

a) Surface Wind.
b) Visibility (or CAVOK).
c) Runway Visual Range (if applicable).
d) Weather.
e) Cloud (or CAVOK).
f) Temperature.
g) Dewpoint.
h) QNH.
I) Recent Weather (if applicable).
j) Wind shear (if applicable).
k) A TREND may be included if a forecaster is on duty.
l) Runway Contamination Warning (if applicable).

Military Aerodromes – weather colour codes

While working a military LARS, or when inbound to a military aerodrome, you may hear the weather being passed as a colour code. This is simply a shorthand method of advising pilots of the surface visibility and base of lowest cloud. The codes for RAF and RN airfields read as follows.

Surface Visibility		**Colour Code**	**Base of lowest cloud layer of 3/8 (SCT) or more**
Km	nm		
8	4.3	Blue	2500 ft AGL
5	2.7	White	1500 ft AGL
3.7	2.0	Green	700 ft AGL
1.6	0.9	Yellow*	300 ft AGL
0.8	0.4	Amber	200 ft AGL
Less than 0.8	Less than 0.4	Red	Below 200 ft AGL or sky obscured
		Black	Aerodrome not usable for reasons other than cloud or visibility minima. Black will precede actual colour code.

* At RN airfields code yellow is sub-divided as follows:

Yellow 1: Visibility 2.5 km (1.4 nm) base of lowest cloud 500 ft.

Yellow 2: Visibility 1.6 km (0.9 nm) base of lowest cloud 300 ft.

* At RAF airfields under the control of HQ11/18 Gp code yellow is sub-divided as follows:

Yellow 1: Visibility 3.7 km (2 nm) base of lowest cloud 500 ft.

Yellow 2: Visibility 1.6 km (0.9 nm) base of lowest cloud 300 ft.

Chapter 18

Meteorological Standards

International Standard Atmosphere

The ISA is a set of figures used to calibrate aircraft instruments or in the specification of aircraft. The main items are:

Pressure at mean sea level – 1013.25 millibars.
Temperature at mean sea level – +15° Centigrade.
Density at mean sea level – 1225 gm/cubic metre.
Temperature lapse rate of – 1.98° C/1000 feet between sea level and the tropopause (averaged at 36,090 feet).
A constant temperature of – minus 56.5° C above the tropopause.

Using these figures manufacturers can test instruments and publish correction formulas for altitudes and environments that depart from the standard conditions.

Reference Humidity

ISA reference humidity is defined as:

a) At temperatures at or below the +15° ISA temperature, 80% relative humidity.

b) At temperatures at or above ISA +28° C (+43°C), 34% relative humidity.

c) At temperatures between ISA and ISA +28° C the relative humidity varies linearly between the humidity specified for those temperatures.

Several other constants are assumed and used regarding aircraft prototypes and certification but are beyond the scope of this book.

Jet Standard Atmosphere

JSA is an internationally agreed set of standards used for instrument design and calibrations:

Mean Sea Level Temperature	+15° C.
Mean Sea Level Pressure	1013.25.
Mean Sea Level Density	1225 grams per cubic metre.
Temperature Lapse Rate	2° per 1000ft with no tropopause.

Glossary of Abbreviations

Not all the following abbreviations are used in UK reports and this list includes some most common ones used worldwide. For a full listing of other aeronautical abbreviations and definitions refer to The *Air Pilot's Glossary and Reference Guide*, also available from Airlife Publishing.

Abbreviation	Meaning
<	Less than.
>	More than.
+	Heavy.
–	Slight.
/	Runway ice or snow not reported.
//	In respect of snow, depth of snow on runway not significant or not measurable. When used to indicate friction coefficient or braking action, braking action not reported.
///	Cloud or visibility; indicates view totally obscured. Temperature or dewpoint; indicated information missing.
0000	Visibility less than 50 metres.
00000	Wind calm.
214	Spot wind chart.
215	UK low level forecast.
216	Decode guide for Metform 215.
9999	Ten kilometres or more.
A	When used in a METAR as a prefix to the pressure, indicates that the figures relate to hundredths of inches of mercury.
AC	Altocumulus.
AIC	Aeronautical Information Circulars.
AIP	Aeronautical Information Publication.

AMD	Used to indicate an amendment to a TAF for its remaining validity period.
AS	Altostratus cloud.
ASSW	Associated with.
AT	At; used in a TAF and followed by a four figure (hours/minutes) time group.
ATC	Air Traffic Control.
ATIS	Automatic Terminal Information Service.
AUTO	Used in a METAR where a fully automated wind report is included.
BC	Fog or mist patches.
BCOP	Broken clouds or better, 5–7 oktas or better.
BECMG	Becoming.
BKN	Broken, 5 to 7 oktas of cloud.
BL	Between layers.
BL	Blowing (snow).
BLDG	Building; an air mass increasing in pressure.
BLO	Below clouds.
BLSN	Blowing snow.
BLU	Blue; weather colour code state for military aerodromes.
BLZD	Blizzard.
BOVC	Base of overcast.
BR	Mist; derived from the French *brouillard*.
BTL	Between layers.
C	Centre runway; when relating to runway visual range.
CAVOK	Ceiling and visibility OK.
CB	Cumulonimbus cloud.
CBR	Cloud Base Recorder.
CC	Cirrocumulus cloud.
CF	Cyclostrophic force.
CI	Cirrus cloud.
CLD	Cloud.
CLRD	Cleared; relating to runways previously contaminated by snow, slush, water or ice.
CLRS	Clear and smooth.
CNS	Continuous, in respect of rain or snow.
COT	Coastal.
CP	Centre of Pressure.
CS	Cirrostratus.
CT	Continental Tropical Air Mass.
CU	Cumulus cloud.
CUF	Cumuliform cloud.

D	Indicates a decreasing tendency when relating to runway visual range.
DALR	Dry Adiabatic Lapse Rate.
DFTS	Downdrafts.
DNS	Dense; in relation to fog, dust or smoke.
DP	Deep; in relation to a low pressure area.
DPNG	Deepening; in relation to a low pressure area.
DR	Low Drifting; used in respect of wind blown snow.
DRFT	Drifting; used in respect of wind blown snow.
DRSN	Low drifting snow.
DS	Dust Storm.
DSIPT	Dissipate.
DTRT	Deteriorating.
DU	Widespread dust.
DUC	Dense upper cloud.
DUR	Duration.
DWN	Downdrafts.
DWPNT	Dewpoint.
DZ	Drizzle.
E	East.
ELR	Environmental Lapse Rate.
EMBD	Embedded; as in cumulonimbus embedded in stratus clouds.
EXTSV	Extensive.
FA	Area meteorological forecast.
FEW	1 to 2 oktas or eighths of cloud coverage.
FC	Funnel cloud, tornado or water-spout.
Fc	Forecast; replaces TAF when used for more than one aerodrome.
FG	Fog.
FLRY	Flurry; as in snow flurries.
FM	From; used in a TAF and followed by a four figure (hours/minutes) time group.
FM	Meteorological service (NOTAM decode 2nd & 3rd letters).
FO	Fog dispersal system (NOTAM decode 2nd & 3rd letters).
FR	Route forecast.
FROPA	Frontal passage.
FROSFC	Frontal surface.
FRQ	Frequent.
FRST	Frost.
FRZ	Freeze.

FRZN	Frozen.
FS	Fracto stratus cloud.
FS	Snow removal equipment (NOTAM decode 2nd & 3rd letters).
FT	Forecast; replaces TAF when used for more than one aerodrome.
FT	Transmissometer (NOTAM decode 2nd & 3rd letters).
FU	Forecast upper winds.
FU	Smoke; derived from the French *fume*.
FW	Wind direction indicator (NOTAM decode 2nd & 3rd letters).
FZ	Freezing or supercooled.
FZDZ	Freezing drizzle.
FZRA	Freezing rain.
G	Gusting; in a METAR gives the maximum gust speed when it exceeds the mean wind speed by 10 kt or more.
GEN	Generally.
GF	Geostrophic Force.
GFDEP	Ground Fog; estimated deep.
GNDFG	Ground Fog.
GR	Hail or soft hail; derived from the German *graupel*.
GRN	Green; weather colour code state for military aerodromes.
GS	Small hail or snow pellets less than 5 mm diameter and/or snow pellets.
GST	Gust.
HC	Covered by compacted snow (NOTAM decode 4th & 5th letters).
HD	Covered by dry snow (NOTAM decode 4th & 5th letters).
HDEP	Haze layer, estimated deep.
HD FRZ	Hard freeze.
HDWND	Head wind.
HE	Covered by water (NOTAM decode 4th & 5th letters).
HF	Totally free of ice and snow (NOTAM decode 4th & 5th letters).
HL	Snow clearance completed (NOTAM decode 4th & 5th letters).
HLSTO	Hailstones.
HLYR	Haze layer aloft.

HO	Obscured by snow (NOTAM decode 4th & 5th letters).
HP	Snow clearance in progress (NOTAM decode 4th & 5th letters).
HR	Standing water (NOTAM decode 4th & 5th letters).
HRCN	Hurricane.
HRS	Hours.
HURCN	Hurricane.
HVY	Heavy.
HY	Snow bank exist (NOTAM decode 4th & 5th letters).
HZ	Covered by frozen ruts and ridges (NOTAM decode 4th & 5th letters).
HZ	Haze.
IAO	In and out of clouds.
IAS	Indicated Air Speed
IC	Ice crystals (Diamond Dust).
ICAO	International Civil Aviation Organisation.
ICE	Icing.
ICGIC	Icing in clouds.
ICICIP	Icing in clouds, in precipitation.
ICGIP	Icing in precipitation.
IFR	Instrument Flight Rules
IMC	Instrument Meteorological Conditions.
IMPR	Improve or improving.
INC	In cloud.
INSTBY	Instability.
INTER	Intermittent.
INTMT	Intermittent.
INTS	Intense.
INTST	Intensity.
INVRN	Inversion.
IOVC	In the overcast.
IPV	Ice on the runway.
IPV	Improve.
IR	Ice on the runway.
IRVR	Instrumented Runway Visual Range.
ISA	International Standard Atmosphere.
ISOL	Isolated.
ISOLD	Isolated.
JET	Jet stream.
JSA	Jet standard atmosphere.
JTST	Jet stream.

K	Kelvin.
KDEF	Smoke layer, estimated deep.
KMH	Kilometres per hour.
KOCTY	Smoke layer over city.
kt	Knot or knots.
KT	Knots, abbreviated in capitals when shown in a TAF or METAR.
L	Left runway; when relating to runway visual range.
LAN	Inland or overland.
LCL	Lifting condensation level.
LCL	Local.
LFC	Level of free convection.
LKLY	Likely.
LLWS	Low level wind shear.
LOC	Locally or localised.
LSQ	Line squall.
LTD	Limited.
LV	Light and variable winds.
LYR	Layer or layered.
M	When quoted in relation to runway visual range relates to the minimum value that can be assessed; used in relation to temperature or dewpoint indicates a negative value.
Ma	Mass flow of air.
MAR	At sea or over the sea, derived from maritime.
mb	Millibar.
MDT	Moderate.
MET	Meteorological or meteorological office.
METAR	Aviation routine weather report (commonly referred to as an actual).
METFAX	Meteorological facsimile.
METFORM	Meteorological proforma.
METFORM 214	UK spot wind and temperature chart.
METFORM 215	UK low level weather chart.
METFORM 216	Decode listing for Metform 215.
MEW	Mean equivalent wind.
MI	Shallow (fog).
MID	Midpoint; in relation to runway visual range.
MIFG	Shallow fog.
MNLD	Mainland.
MOD	Moderate.
MOGR	Moderate or greater.
MON	Above mountains.

MOV	Moving.
MP	Maritime Polar Air Mass.
MPS	Metres per second.
MRGL	Marginal.
m/s	Metres per second.
MS	Minus.
MSA	Minimum Sector Altitude.
MSL	Mean Sea Level.
MSTR	Moisture.
MT	Maritime tropical air.
MTI	Marked temperature inversion.
MTW	Mountain waves.
MVFR	Marginal Visual Flight Rules.
MWO	Meteorological Watch Office.
MX	Mixed types of ice (white and clear).
MXD	Mixed.
N	Indicates no distinct change; when relating to runway visual range.
N	North.
NCWX	No change in weather.
NE	North-East.
NMRS	Numerous.
NOSIG	No significant change.
NOTAM	Notice to Airmen.
NS	Nimbostratus Cloud.
NSC	No significant cloud.
NSW	No significant weather.
NW	North-West.
OBS	Observed; observation.
OBSC	Obscured.
OCFNT	Occluded front.
OCLN	Occlusion.
OCNL	Occasional.
OFP	Occluded frontal passage.
OFSHR	Offshore.
OMTNS	Over mountains.
ONSHR	Onshore.
OPA	Opaque, white ice.
OPMET	Operational meteorological (information).
OPT	On top.
OT	On top.
OVC	Overcast.

P	Pressure.
PBL	Probable; probability.
PCPN	Precipitation.
PE	Ice pellets.
PFG	Pressure gradient force.
PIC	Potential icing category.
PO	Dust devil or sand whirls.
PR	Partially covering, in respect of fog coverage at an aerodrome.
PRES	Pressure.
PRESFR	Pressure falling rapidly.
PRESSRR	Pressure rising rapidly.
PROB	Probability, in percentage terms.
PS	Plus (+).
PSR	Packed snow on runway.
PTCHY	Patchy; mist or fog.
Q Codes	There are numerous ICAO Q codes relating to weather, for a full listing refer to DOC 8400/4 available from CAA Stationery; the most commonly used are listed below.
QFE	Altimeter setting to display height above aerodrome surface.
QFF	The QFE reduced to a mean sea level value by using actual temperature and pressure conditions; it is used by meteorological units for plotting synoptic charts.
QNE	The height that the altimeter will show on landing at an airfield with 1013mb set.
QNH	Altimeter setting to display altitude above sea level.
QUH	Current barometric pressure at sea level.
R	Runway (followed by the designation number) when relating to Runway Visual Range.
R	Right runway; when relating to runway visual range.
RA	Rain.
RAF	Royal Air Force.
RAFC	Regional Area Forecast Centre.
RAFL	Rainfall.
RAPID	Rapid or rapidly; a change expected to occur in half an hour or less.
RAREP	Radar weather report.
RASH	Rain showers.
RASN	Rain and snow.
RCN	Runway condition reading.
RDG	Ridge of high pressure.

RE	Recent; as in recent weather.
REDZ	Recent drizzle.
REFRA	Recent freezing rain.
REGR	Recent hail, GR is derived from the German *graupel.*
RERA	Recent rain.
RESH	Recent showers.
RESN	Recent snow.
RETS	Recent thunderstorm.
RGN	Region.
RH	Relative humidity.
RMK	Remark.
RN	Royal Navy.
ROFOR	Route forecast.
RPD	Rapid.
RSG	Rising.
RVR	Runway Visual Range.
S	South.
SA	Dust storm or sandstorm.
SA	When followed by a date and time, used to signify that a METAR or SPECI consists of reports for one or more aerodromes.
SALR	Saturated Adiabatic Lapse Rate.
SC	Stratocumulus cloud.
SCAN	Surface Condition Analyser.
SCOB	Scattered cloud or better, 3 - 4 oktas or less.
SCT	Scattered, 3 – 4 oktas of cloud coverage.
SCWD	Supercooled Water Droplets.
SE	South-east.
SEV	Severe; in relation to icing or turbulence.
SFLOC	Sferic location; the position of lightning flashes determined by radio triangulation.
SG	Snow grains.
SH	Shower(s).
SHLW	Shallow; as in fog.
SHWR	Shower.
SIGMET	Significant meteorological information.
SIGWX	Significant weather.
SKC	Sky clear.
SLGT	Slight.
SLO	Slow.
SLR	Slush on runway.
SLT	Sleet.
SMK	Smoke.
SMTH	Smooth.

SN	Snow.
SNFLK	Snowflakes.
SNOCLO	Message relating to an aerodromes's closure due to snow.
SNOWTAM	A special NOTAM relating to snow, ice slush or water.
SNSH	Snow showers.
SNW	Snow.
SNWFL	Snowfall.
SP	When followed by a date and time, used to signify that a METAR or SPECI consists of reports for one or more aerodromes.
SPECI	Aviation selected special weather report.
SPECIAL	Special meteorological report, in plain language.
SPOT	Spot wind at a specific location.
SPRD	Spread.
SQ	Squalls.
SQAL	Squall.
SQLN	Squall line.
SS	Sandstorm.
ST	Stratus cloud.
Stf	Stratiform cloud.
STM	Storm.
STNR or STNRY	Stationary; used in relation to a front.
Sts	Stratus cloud.
SV	VOLMET forecast (NOTAM decode 2nd & 3rd letters).
SW	South-west.
SYNOP	Internationally coded synoptic weather chart.
SYRED	Internationally coded synoptic weather chart of reduced length.
t	Trend landing forecast.
T	Temperature in degrees Kelvin.
TAF	Terminal Aerodrome Forecast.
TAIL	Tailwind.
TC	Tropical Cyclone.
TCU	Towering cumulonimbus cloud.
TDO	Tornado.
TDWR	Terminal Doppler weather radar.
TEMP	Temperature.
TEMPO	Temporarily, a change lasting less than one hour.
TEND	Tend or tending to.
THDR	Thunder.
THK	Thick, as in fog.

THN	Thin, as in mist or fog.
THSD	Thousand.
TL	Until; used in a TAF and followed by a four figure (hours/minutes) time group.
TLWD	Tailwind.
TMPRY	Temporary.
TNDCY	Tendency.
TOP	Cloud top.
TOVC	Top of overcast cloud.
TREND	Landing forecast for two hours after the observation time.
TROF	Trough of low pressure.
TROP	Tropopause.
TRS	Tropical Cyclone.
TS	Thunderstorm.
TSGR	Thunderstorm with hail; GR is derived from the German *graupel*.
TSHWR	Thundershower.
TSQLS	Thundersqualls.
TSSA	Thunderstorms with associated dust or sand storm.
TSTM	Thunderstorm.
TURB	Turbulence.
TWEB	Transcribed weather broadcast.
TYPH	Typhoon.
U	Indicates an increasing tendency; when relating to runway visual range.
UDDF	Up and downdrafts.
U_{DF}	Speed of vertical gust.
UK	United Kingdom.
UTC	Universal Coordinated Time.
V	When relating to runway visual range V is used to separate the minimum and maximum values if the variations fall within predetermined criteria.
V	Variable; used in a METAR when a wind speed greater that 3kt varies by 60° or more in the 10 minutes preceding the time of observation.
VA	Volcanic Ash.
VAL	In valleys.
VAS	Vortex Advisory System.
VC	In vicinity; within 8km of an aerodrome perimeter, but not at the aerodrome.
VCY	Vicinity.

VER	Vertical.
VERVIS	Vertical visibility.
VFR	Visual Flight Rules
VIS	Visibility.
VLNT	Violent.
VMC	Visual Meteorological Conditions.
VOLMET	Very High Frequency meteorological report.
VR	Veer.
VRB	Variable (wind).
VSBY	Visibility.
VSP	Vertical speed.
VV	Vertical visibility; VV/// indicates the vertical visibility cannot be assessed.
VWS	Vortex Wake System.
W	West.
WAFC	World Area Forecast Centre.
WDI	Wind direction indicator.
WDSPR	Widespread.
WEA	Weather.
WFP	Warm front passage.
WHT	White; weather colour code state for military aerodromes.
WINTEM	Forecast upper wind and temperatures.
WK	Weak.
WKN	Weaken or weakening.
WMO	World Meteorological Office.
WND	Wind.
WRM	Warm.
WRMFRNT	Warm front.
WRNG	Warning.
WS	Wind shear.
WSHFT	Wind shift.
WTSPT	Water spout.
W/V	Wind velocity.
WV	Wave.
WX	Weather.
XX	Heavy.
Z	Zulu Time.
Zulu	Greenwich Mean Time.

Index